Best Lesbian Erotica
1998

Selected and Introduced by Jenifer Levin

Tristan Taormino, Series Editor

CLEIS
PRESS

Best Lesbian Erotica 1998

Selected and Introduced by Jenifer Levin

Tristan Taormino, Series Editor

"Box 309"© 1998 by Jane DeLynn is excerpted from her novel Box 309. Excerpts of "Cleo's Gone" by Gwendolyn Bikis first appeared in *Close Calls* edited by Susan Fox Rogers (New York: St. Martin's Press, 1996) and *Does Your Mama Know?* edited by Lisa C. Moore (Redbone Press, 1997); an earlier version appeared in *The Persistent Desire* edited by Joan Nestle (Boston: Alyson Publications, 1992). "Clubs" © 1994 by Kim Yaged first appeared in *Bad Attitude* (1994). "Clash of the Titans" ©1997 by Karlyn Lotney first appeared in *Virgin Territory 2* edited by Shar Rednour (New York: Richard Kasak Books, 1997).

Contents

Acknowledgments

I would like to thank the following people for their contributions to the book: To Frédérique Delacoste, Felice Newman, and everyone at Cleis Press for continuing to make things happen! To Jenifer Levin for her tremendous work under difficult circumstances, and Amber Hollibaugh for keeping us both a little more sane. To Heather Lewis, Jewelle Gomez, Richard Labonté, and all the contributors of the 1996 and 1997 collections for being an ongoing part of the series. Special thanks to the folks at bookstores, especially the independents, who continue to support, promote, and host events for the book.

To Tom Bates, Kate Bornstein, Bree Coven, Morgan Dunbar, Fish, Gerry Gomez Pearlberg, Karen Green, Mario Grillo, Colin Hall, Ron Lieber, Audrey Prins-Patt, Janet Schomer, D. Travers Scott and David Eckard, Don Spargo, Jr., Michael Tauber, and Winston Wilde for their love, kisses, hugs, support, slack, understanding, sweets, favors, dinners, voice mail messages, patience, and generosity. Huge thanks to Carol Queen for being one of my most important role models. To my mom for being another one. And to Reggie Love and Jordan Love for early-morning wake-up calls, blissful trips to the park, and other adventures in dog raising.

Foreword

As the saying goes, the third time's the charm. In the case of lesbian erotica in the nineties, more likely the talisman or the fetish. The third incarnation of *Best Lesbian Erotica* is unique, as were its predecessors, and this time around there is an additional difference. The majority of the submissions and nominations we received this year were not from well-known writers. So in the 1998 list of contributors, you'll see few famous authors or "big names." In fact, some writers even noted in their short biographies that the contribution marked their first ever published work or their first published erotic work. We're proud that this collection introduces a new group of lesbian writers to the world.

Where did they come from? The submissions came to me from as far away as Japan and as close as a few blocks from my home in Brooklyn. More symbolically, they came from the desire and the courage to write about the erotic. They also came from our foremothers, women whose work paved the way for what is now an entire genre of erotica. Some of the first lesbian writers to put sex on the page, women who have inspired and encouraged erotic writing, were Joan Nestle, Cherríe Moraga, and Pat Califia. These pioneers and others have been role models for many of us.

Similarly, the relationship between the guest judge (who selects and introduces the pieces) and me (the series editor) is one of teaching, learning, and mentoring. I have the chance to learn a tremendous amount—about writing, editing, and being part of a larger community of queer writers—from writers who have made significant contributions to lesbian literature. I also have the unique opportunity to explore multiple issues about erotica as part of the process of creating the book.

Each year, the guest judge and I approach this concept called *lesbian erotica* and the task of choosing the *best lesbian erotica* of the year from very different perspectives. One of the inherent differences between us is generational. These women—Heather Lewis, Jewelle Gomez, Jenifer Levin—lived the Lesbian Sex Wars. They wrestled with critical sex issues in their relationships, their communities, and their writing. Their writing was and is informed by an early lack of erotic images, conflicts over erotic representation, and an important turning point in lesbian history. I am the quintessential post–Sex War baby, coming out amid *On Our Backs,* Susie Bright, Good Vibrations, and sex zines. When I started writing queer smut, I had the luxury of reading what was already out there and the privilege of not being the first one to do it.

Another difference at play in the dynamic between guest editor and series editor is our own backgrounds. Our histories are informed by where we came from and where we are now, and those places must be respected and bridged. The butch-femme bars, passing women, and underground communities of life and literature have paved the way for sex clubs, dyke daddies, and fisting workshops.

And finally, there is the question of taste. Taste is an elusive concept. More than once during each of the selection processes, Heather, Jewelle, or Jenifer and I turned to one another puzzled and asked, "You like *what ?*" And even when reviews try to boil down this issue to *Heather Lewis likes her erotica dark and violent* or *Jewelle Gomez likes hers poetic and multicultural,* it is always more complex than that. It has been rewarding to explore the complexities. It has been a challenge to try to communicate what turns me on as a writer and a woman and to understand what arouses other women.

During our meetings and correspondence, the discussion, banter, and explanations of why we like what we like were the most interesting parts of the process. These dialogues of perspective and difference mirror the intangible dialogues between the contributors and the readers of the books. What turns us on, what rings true, what works...what turns us off, what we don't understand, what doesn't touch us, is all part of this communication between writer and reader, between tutor and pupil. Likewise, reading the many submissions we get every year has provided an interesting window into the erotic lives—both real and imagined—of women all over the world. There is such incredible diversity in subject, in form, in style, and in the ways in which these writers approach the erotic.

The stories in *Best Lesbian Erotica 1998* reflect this diversity. There is a varied cast of characters, including sassy basketball players, S/M novices and experts, and butches with endless swaggers and hard-ons. There's a girl who dresses like a boy and a girl who became a boy, a girl who loves shopping and a girl who likes to lick boots. Girls with goals and girls on a mission. They come together to form fascinating pairs: a security guard and a shoplifter, a vegetarian and a carnivore, a city transit worker and a charitable nun. They are intrigued and excited by a pair of stolen panties, nuns' habits, drops of water, and other powerful, aphrodisiac objects. They have messy sex, religious sex, and genderbending sex. These are stories of secret trysts, first times and last times, games of luck and lust and chance.

The more we write about our passions and pleasures, the more we can learn about ourselves and one another. Creating these collections has always been an invaluable learning experience for me. I hope the series is also valuable to those who read it. As readers, you are part of the writers' journeys and adventures. You are their subjects, objects, muses, senseis, and protégés. Crawl under the cover, between the pages, and let the lessons begin.

Tristan Taormino
New York
November 1997

Introduction

Gentle readers,

Rough riders,

I have to be honest and say that I almost did not make it here alive this year.

That's no comment on the quality of the writing in this volume! Rather, it's a true statement about the nature of my own life right now, as I enter the very middle of it...having just emerged tentatively from an extended and wretched period of time, in which a seemingly endless compendium of problems on all fronts practical and personal—and I don't mean minor woes, girls, I mean real life crises—took me by the jugular and refused to let go. Now, you know how it is: when you're hurt and angry and sick and frightened and ashamed and in all kinds of pain, one of the last things on your mind is sex. So it should come as no surprise when I tell you that it was a stretch for me to sit down and read a bunch of erotica.

But I'm glad I did. And here's why.

Sex is an act of love and rage and joy and defiance and life. Lesbian identity, for me, has always been inextricably enmeshed with queer sexuality; I couldn't ever see my own queer self existing in quite the same way, self-defined and defined by the world, without the practice of queer sex being part and parcel of the human package...as passionately and as often as possible. Yes, Dorothy, homosexuality is about sex; it is about difference; it is about loneliness. It is about having the courage to be your unique human self despite the great cost. And these stories reminded me of all that. They reminded me that I am alive.

Most anthologies purport to be thematic. But I always did feel that that requirement put the cart before the horse. The truth is that any collection of short stories presents its own themes. So, when we sent out a call for submissions this year, we kept the thematic stuff to a minimum. Aside from the general requirements of the erotica genre itself, we had but a few requests for our authors: we were interested in publishing as many good new writers as possible; we were interested in writing that stayed away from fruit and flower metaphors; and we were interested in stories that pulled the reader into the real "hands-on" feel of sex. Most of all, we were interested in choosing the best-written tales of the bunch. And so we did.

I never doubted that this collection would trumpet its own themes loudly and clearly. Transgression—to my mind, a hallmark of genuine queer literature—turns out to be a big one, the "umbrella" theme, if you will. A lot of these stories are subtly transgressive; some are anything but. Some, in fact, have all the transgressive subtlety of fucking in the bushes at a grief-besotted funeral. Along these lines, the overt exercise of power, gender-fuck, dominance, and surrender are everywhere in your face. And even though it takes at least two to tango, many of these voices are solitary, outlaw voices at heart. Most of these characters, by implication, have survived despite the world—and, in some cases, despite themselves. They don't hide their actions or their needs. The raw physical sweat and effort of sexual honesty matters here, as well as the elements of sport and play. And where there is not overt humor and celebration, there is a corresponding determination and irony.

A few of the writers presented here are widely anthologized, well-published by both mainstream and small presses. I'm proud to be able to include their newest and freshest work. But most of the contributors have never been published before. This makes me happy. It means that, in the world of lesbian erotic fiction, we aren't chronically recycling ourselves. And there's a new generation of queer women writing unabashedly about the truth, pain, and fun of the queer sexual experience—in all its variety, its surprising twists and turns, its rich psychological depth. These gals are not afraid to fuck or be fucked. They are not afraid to just go out and get it. And when opportunity rears its pretty head, they generally don't hesitate. In fact, they tend to ask "Why not?!" instead of "Why?" Ah. The calling card of youth.

But who ever said longing should remain unfulfilled?

Take this book to bed with you tonight. Unless you have someone to take to bed with you tonight; in which case, forget the fucking book for now. But whenever you choose to read it, I think you will be entranced, enhanced, enlightened, turned on, disturbed, engaged. Key word—engaged. Whether or not you identify with the sexual stances presented here, you will be engaged by each and every piece of written work.

All of which is a lengthy way of saying: Enjoy it, girlfriends!

Enjoy.

Jenifer Levin
New York City
November 1997

Making Girls Come

Carellin Brooks

Me and my friends, it's all we ever want to do. We argue about it, compare notes, strategize. We are like generals planning incursions into other countries, places we've never been. Foreign correspondents. Soldiers of fortune. We run bombing missions, go undercover, crack codes. Anything it takes.

One girl I knew always needed a wall to lean against. Something solid, she said. I'd look up and see her hands, sightless, groping. Right here I would have said but my mouth was full.

Some of them, she can see it's like a fist, that same movement open and clenched over & over. In the end it's one last push & then they curl up, head down, eyes closed. Turn away.

The rhythm. Stop and start and then I lose it again. The pause, like stuttering in the middle of a line. Composing sentences. Phantom typewriters. A baby grand playing by itself, in the middle of a room, on a dais on the floor. The crescendo, falling.

Sometimes she thinks she could just do it and do it for them over and over and then again. Any of them. Anyone at all. The best is doing it for them. The second best is watching.

We argue about it all the time.

"It's the rhythm," I say, putting down my glass for emphasis. Everyone has her own theory. We all want to be experts in this bar.

Another girl shakes her head. "You just have to know."

"I'd like to just do it one after the other, a whole roomful of them," says somebody else.

I smile, lift my glass.

Then there's that thing about noise. You can never trust anybody who's too quiet. I remember a girl who used to bang on the wall, not because the next-door neighbor moaned so much but because the moans were so regulated. Came so predictably.

She likes it when they're fast. The way they bear down, the way their mouths open. She drinks it all in. Sometimes she wants to count. To stop it. "Okay, now," she says, and they let go in a flood.

Then there are the girls who never come at all.

"Doesn't bother me," they say.

"It's no big deal."

"I don't know why everybody makes such a fuss about it," they snap, turning over, irritated, rearranging the covers. We wait it out, quiet, pretending unconcern. We project a disinterested helpfulness, nothing more. We can always try, we say if they ask. We shrug our shoulders as if it doesn't matter, it's not important. Might as well give it a shot. After all, we do have experience. We've done it before. Our manner is perfect. We conceal our gaping need, our burning impatience so well, we almost forget it ourselves.

But we don't fool them.

They don't ask.

They know what we want.

Some of them, it's like a wave takes them & sucks them under & back. Through the deep blue until they're lifting their heads, pulling for air like they're being born again. Their eyes when they finally open them are just that color of water, grown calm.

"Like this?" I say.

"Like this?" I watch her for clues, watch her foreign body. I can do this all night, I promise her. Anything it takes. Anything.

"No," she says, impatient. She turns from me, but I don't have time to feel aggrieved; there's something else I want more than pride, more than proof.

"Show me, then," I say, and she does, the gift, the gift.

So many of them, it's a fight from the start. She sees the battle in their faces. Don't do that. You're wasting time. It'll never happen. She watches them pause and dip and try to still the voices & concentrate. She feels them waver, there on the end of her fingers, like water across a lens.

"On the floor, in the kitchen."

"When it's all sweaty and you're sliding back and forth."

"Me on the floor, her standing up. Her weight on me."

"Inside of her. That's the best. Inside of her and her on top so you can watch the whole thing."

"Sometimes you can't imagine how when you first see her, when she's looking so buttoned-up, you could never even guess. Then you find out. You never would have known."

"It doesn't matter how. Just that they let you. Just that you can be there."

It's the look they give you. That drowning, gasping, who-are-you look. The stripped look of someone who's gone too far. C'mon honey, she says then. Yes.

For one second everything stops. There is no outside or inside or even in-between. There is only us in this room, me and you saying yes yes and nobody else at all in the world.

She likes to do it. It's a job. It's a calling. It's even, in the pleasantest of senses, a duty. She feels the responsibility in her hands, in the line of her arm, in her interview smile. Trust me, her smile says when she turns back and sees another girl, dark hair, just watching, across the bar. She gets up.

"Hi," I say.

"Hi," the dark-haired girl says, lifting one eyebrow, all mouth and attitude. It's my assignment. I take it gladly.

Juice

Tee Chandler

Juice oozes from the corner of her mouth and then settles in greasy suspension. Swallowing the last of her burger, my woman slides her rapacious tongue along her full lips, absorbing grease and the flavor of hour-old pussy juice.

I feel repulsed. Her sweet blackberry eyes fling back a look of defiance. She knows I will not kiss her dead animal mouth until she has cleansed it, eradicating the barbarism of her lunch. I knock over my fork-built tower of cold onion rings. They lie arranged within the ketchup like sixties wallpaper. I reflect how once, despite my protests, my disgust, she ate a hot dog while she prepared to mount me, having made me wait with my hands fettered, her behavior as coarse as the handcuffs. Recollecting the smell and texture of her kiss turns my stomach. I should not have anything to do with her. Her habits are grotesque.

Sometimes I think that she investigated my aversions before I got to know her—that she is some kind of wretched agent from hell. A test of my will, my power.

I pull out my wallet and count out enough change to pay for our snack. She sits back, eyes still amused, and watches me as I walk around and pull out her chair as she stands up. The smell of animal fat hangs around her head, and I instantly breathe through my mouth. I follow her out onto the street, pissed off at her callous soul. If indeed she has a soul.

She requested this morning that I wear my suit—my one and only. I obliged and got decked out in a sharp Armani suit, bought secondhand two years ago. Immediately, I assumed that our date was going to be a grand event. It is rare that she wants me in anything but jeans, a shirt, and the leather jacket I wear only in her presence. I hate it—animal skin, flayed and decayed. The inside pocket contains lube and condoms. There is more leather—straps nagging at my cunt support a dildo snug against my just-tight-enough jeans. Those jeans, her choice, were a spontaneous purchase a couple of months ago.

She pulled me into a denim emporium on Oxford Street, pulled out her choice and then sat on the wooden stairs, winking at the guy as I paid for them. She revels in the perversity of her sexuality. Only minutes before, in the changing cubicle, she had been riding my face to the point of suffocation, digging her nails into the back of my head to divert the tension of not crying out. I just managed to grab the selected jeans before she wiped my face clean with them.

The battle is constant between the indignities she causes me and the kick that I get out of her behavior. With her, I am learning so much. Not just about sex, but about myself, my spiritual limits. And the exploration of both repulsion and addiction.

Striding swiftly to catch up with her, I letch at her arse, feeling it snaking around my dick with each curve of her step. In her black satin Blahnik heels, she is very female, very dangerous. I am conscious of my latex rod and grab at it through my pocket. Suddenly, she turns and pushes me backward. I struggle to keep my balance, hoping for a piece of wall or shop front to catch my weight. She comes toward me again, and I wait for the humiliation of crashing to my arse in front of her—devoid of dignity, publicly at her mercy. Her hands lunge for my jacket and pull me toward her. And then she pushes again, this time keeping her hands tight on my lapels. Smiling, sour blackberry eyes. I turn my head to seek a prop, then return to her gaze, smiling a little myself. I see an alley. A piss-stink alley that runs alongside a pub. As we bundle toward the rear of it, her hands unzip me, before I land roughly and intentionally on a beer keg. She squats to sit astride me, too wet and impatient to use a condom, her tits hanging out in my face. My mouth clings onto them as she fucks me. They jiggle deliciously, slut-tits.

"Suck them, butch, suck them hard like a hungry baby while I fuck myself to a fat orgasm."

She leans into me, her head flung back, and there is nothing but her breasts.

I am delirious with greed to get her bullet nipples in my mouth. I hear her hiss—she is on her way. My legs are pushing against the wall, creating a tension that can handle the punishment she is giving out. She comes loudly over a background sound of Irish country music that seeps from the pub toilet window.

As she studies her fingers, a frown scribbles across her forehead. Her forefinger is a little bloody, and she pokes it in my mouth to suck.

"Sorry baby, did I scratch you? Did my nails draw blood? Let me kiss you better."

She puckers her mouth and blows a kiss to the injuries at the top of my back, while I contentedly treat her finger to a blow job. So tender sometimes. As her obnoxious predilections fade, the urge to fuck her and make babies together gets the better of me.

"Marry me?" I hope.

She stands before me, rolling her nipples, tall against the summer-gray sky. My sex amazon. Her skirt is still around her hips, pussy lips just glistening through her coarse hair. Her cunt taunts me as she lifts a leg onto my lap. The black satin heel is digging into my thigh. Pinching myself is unnecessary—I know I'm in heaven. Bittersweet blackberry eyes.

"Huh!" comes the sneer; she's an archfiend in an instant.

I shuffle behind her, simultaneously trying to keep up and straighten my clothing. There have been times when she's accused me of never living life for the moment, like it was gonna run out and leave me stranded, suspended between visions of possibilities.

"Puppet-boy," she jibes, happy to be the puppet-mistress, pulling the strings and dropping me as her whim dictates. I hesitate to call her cruel; the word feels too clichéd for her behavior.

"Two one-twenties, please."

The bus conductor slaps the ticket into my hand. Perhaps he smells her cunt juice on both of us. He is rude. London city rude, or just offended, I don't know.

We sit in silence, symbiotically observing various scenes of life from the top deck of the bus. The Saturday masses at the Angel give way to the quieter back roads of de Beauvoir, as we leave the bus route and walk the few hundred meters to my home.

Her ascent up the stairs to my front door is blessed, her backside inciting me to open the door urgently. I lead her through the front door, a good butch checking for intruders lurking in the shadows.

"Are you gonna be good to me, baby?" I ask, almost plead. She looks at me vacantly, reclining on my bed, the midnight blue cotton already stained from a week ago—the smell too good to wash away. Grinding her hips, her buttocks pushing into the mattress, her fingerings preparing the way for me.

"You want me to fuck you, honey?" reverence in my voice. "Want me to be a good butch for you? I'll do that. I'll fuck you hard like a woman needs. Real hard, like you want it. I won't even ask you anymore."

Standing naked but for my cock, I slide on a rubber and caress the lube all over it. It is performance art, the way I treat my clitdick. She wants to beg me; I can see it in the tension of her mouth, the way she bites her lip, holding back the demand.

"Good girl."

It is my time now. I reach for a tissue to drag hard against her mouth, absorbing the residue of lipstick and animal fat. For three months I have allowed her to make the moves, and I've obeyed her sexual demands. Now, it is my turn. I lean over her to trace her smudged mouth, energy crackling from my fingertips, then shocking me as I dip into her very wet cunt.

She remains on her back, which surprises me. I'm unsure if she might change her mind. Relinquishing sexual power must be hard for her—high femmes are such schemers. Yet here she is, a good mission-ary girl—on her back, legs wide, wide, arms down by her sides, hips grinding, seeking deliverance.

I will be her benefactor and give her the fuck she craves—on my terms. I climb on top of her like I have watched people do a thousand times before in the porn cinema I frequent. The sounds she makes become echoes of those faceless celluloid women flashing in my head. I immediately start driving into her. The bed fusses and pulses with the floorboards and walls, an orchestra of need and devotion. I stare at her as she sinks into another place, feel the electricity of her power and my own. Sweat from my face drops onto her lips, the salt making her thirstier. I thrust, lunge heavily into her, and wish I had chosen the big-ger dildo to feed her voracious hole and the pictures in my mind. The images fall like an out-of-control elevator to my cuntprick. I am slam-ming her now, on a collision course to coming, as her legs wrap around me, clasping for deeper penetration. Gasps and grunts greet my ears. I lean on one arm, biceps pumped up with the strain, and grab at her breast. My mouth is by her jugular, sucking flesh to stop my own sounds of gluttony. The friction of momentum and leather on my cunt is urging me to erupt within her. She will scream tonight.

"I'm fuckin' you, woman, I'm fuckin' you." But the words drop from my mouth in scorn, not the intended reverence. I don't know how it happened. She stops moving. The porn princesses are extinguished from my mind.

"No."

My dick stays hard as my clit shrivels. She sits up and pushes her beautiful tits back into her bra. As she leans over to reach for her sweater, her arsehole is taut and taunting.

"I'm sorry, I didn't mean..."

I had gone too far. I had been deluded, self-hypnotized into thinking that this time I was in control. I had disrespected her femmeness by allowing her to sense my delusion of being in control.

Turning the bathroom light off, after an absence of a few minutes and an audible orgasm, she walks over to me. I want to suck the fresh lipstick from her mouth, but instead I lower my eyes as she shakes her head and ruffles my hair.

"I'll call you...When I have a need."

"Please, yes...please." Please don't withdraw your favors, I want to beg—I'll be good and do as you say, mistress, mistress, mistress. In my panic, the semantics of masochism hit the spot—a route to forgiveness, to achieving.

The door shuts firmly behind her—I flinch, then slide into the duvet, mournful. My head is filled with all manner of begging and groveling. Resisting the ease of self-pity, I scan for the lessons to be learned from this, and know I will be a better butch for it. She is my woman, but relentless in her insistence on etiquette and a partner who understands the intricacies of femme control.

In resurrection, my clit persuades me to pursue some comfort. I give the lube another squeeze, then stroke efficiently to orgasm, my nose against a pale stain on the bed.

I will learn. She will call me.

Every Boy

Dorian Key

Every boy has his beginnings, some starting place, a point of conception. My boy evolution started long ago: every time I was called "young man" in the barber shop; every time I saw myself in the mirror and realized I looked more and more like a picture I had of my teenaged grandfather, a sweet pretty boy with a severe haircut; every time some chickenhawk fag cruised my ass, it really sunk in, stuck me hard with a needle of perverse stickiness.

"Please, Daddy," I utter. Your hand clenches my shoulder and you breathe in roughly, quickly. And then I descend further into my new life as you shove me down until my chin touches the glossy wood floor. From there all I can see is your boots, for which I start the lowest possible approach. Your boots, boots I want to lick and suck, sweetly, voraciously, in the same way I want to move my mouth and tongue over your daddy-cock. I crawl with my elbows bent out, my bare stomach and chest sliding across the cool floor, my ass rounded in the air. I again look up at you, my daddy, finally looming over me, stroking the bulge in your Levi's. I wait trembling, my lips opening hungrily; slightly and for several long beats, you lock gazes with me as you continue stroking yourself.

Until your deep whisper, "Kiss them," frees me.

Relieved, I murmur thickly, "Thank you, Sir," and then lean forward until my lips graze the gleaming black surface covering your right foot. Then, with a hint of swollen tongue, my mouth skims the pungent smoothness.

"Boy!" you snap, "I want to *feel* you working!"

"Yes, Sir," I mumble into your boot. I press harder, my lips becoming tender against the firm leather as I work from your left to your right foot, but your impatient exhalation of breath tells me that you're not happy, yet. My kisses become pure pressure as I try to give you more sensation, until you hiss, "Use your teeth, boy!"

"Y-yes s-Sir, thank you, Sir," and I eagerly dig my small, sharp teeth into your boot.

Your whisper breathes out, "That's right."

Encouraged, I outline your foot with my mouth and teeth, teeth that are happy to bite, to sink into something so good. Teeth that focus my frustrated young energy into a wild animal cling. And cling to you I do, losing myself in my jaw's grip on my daddy, losing myself in the boy I am becoming, who like a pup nips and clutches desperately for attention.

"Stop," you growl. "You've got to leave some space for other marks."

Panting and trembling, I drop from my lock on you, a difficult thing for a boy who didn't even know he so desperately needed a daddy until earlier that evening.

"What I'm really looking for," you said, leaning back comfortably in you chair at the café as the lines on your handsome face deepened around your broad smile, "is a boy."

Clutching my cooling cup, I jerked out of my well-practiced coffee house slouch to prime attention as my good boy with good posture zinged into every bit of my being. All it takes is for me to hear a gorgeous older butch-boy, such as yourself, utter those beautiful words.

"W-well," I sputtered. Unable to articulate clearly, a rare thing for my wordy self, I struggled on, "Uh, uh, I-uh..." Finally I gave up and awkwardly gestured toward myself, myself being a tall, lean boy-dyke with a military haircut and an angular pretty-boy face, then taken over by a smile of delight and the extreme happy desire to please.

You ignored my offering and continued, "And what I really want to do is play *daddy* and boy."

My attempt to swallow some coffee halted abruptly as I gagged and coughed on misdirected liquid. When my coughing continued, you stood, moved closer to me, and hit me on my back a few times. Finally my choking stopped and, red-faced, I looked up into your concerned paternal gaze. Then you smiled and said, "Good boy, *good* boy. Let Daddy help you."

"Oh god, yes," I said thickly, slowly allowing this to begin. "Please do, Daddy, please help me," and I permitted my needy words and starving gaze to seek from you what I then knew I wanted, and must work hard to prove I deserved. You leaned down, disengaged my hands from the mug, took them in yours and pulled me up, helping me to stand on suddenly wobbly legs. And then it was me, with a beaming face, looking down at your short, white-blond hair and intent face. You reached up and sweetly traced the line of my smooth jaw with your fingertips and then moved down to clasp my right hand. With a sudden tug, you pulled me toward the door.

The cold night air cleared my head and my normally talkative self returned. "Gosh, I've always been into boy-on-boy stuff, but I never really thought of *daddy* and boy until you mentioned it. And I must say, it certainly sounds appealing." I continued on in a quick ramble of words and you smiled indulgently at me, you, my teacher of so many things, now guiding me into a new lesson.

I chattered on excitedly until we got to your place, but my voice quieted as soon as the door thudded behind us. Again I felt that pained, embarrassing inability to articulate anything of sense. "Uh, uh..."

"What's wrong? Can't talk?" You smiled, secure in knowing exactly what it takes to shut me up, what it takes to give my overly active mind something to wrestle with and impede my power of speech.

And I was mind-wrestling with this daddy-boy image of you and me, which crowded my thoughts in enclosed spaces with you so near. So close that your breath grazed my cold face as you tilted your head up and pulled me toward you. Your lips deliberately, smoothly pressed into mine as you eased me slightly open, open enough for you to dart your small, sweet tongue into my mouth. I breathed in your taste deeply and you pulled back, smiling wickedly at my thoroughly dumbstruck self.

Now it is the heady scent of your wet, well-marked leather boots that I breathe in, savoring the taste, savoring the end of my wait.

"Boy," your soft voice triggers my heart and mouth, both overly eager to work their way around you over and over. And you let me try by saying, "Show me how much you want Daddy's cock."

I move back, stretch my body flat on the floor, and reach out to you with my hands. Then I begin pulling myself toward you, slowly, dragging my belly, and my breasts with painfully stiff nipples, across the cold floor. As I close the distance between us, my mouth seeks out blindly, by taste, where you begin and your boot-tips end. Lightly skimming over the spit-shined boots with my lips and tongue, I move up to the tops of your laces. Then I angle my head up to look at you. With the slightest nod you encourage me to continue. I pull in a deep breath and clasp my hands around the backs of your legs and slowly follow with my grasping, hungry lips. The dull, dry texture of your jeans fills my mouth, making me want your dick, slick with my spit, even more. I suck and pull myself hand over hand, lip after lip up your firm thighs to where they join and your jeans try to hide my destination. As my hands squeeze your ass, my mouth tests and begs softly and then harder as I press my teeth and tongue against your bulge. Your hands rest on your black leather-belted hips as you watch me work, as you watch me try to show you how much I want my daddy's cock. And I *really* want it, as my escaping whimpers testify.

"Boy, *tell* me how much you want it. Beg me."

"Sir," my voice cracks. I clear my throat and try again. "Please, Sir, let me suck your cock. I need it so much." You gaze down at me, weighing my request. "Please, please, Sir!" I plead.

"Well," you answer, "I'm not sure if you really deserve it."

"Oh god, Sir, Daddy, please. I'll do *anything!* Just let me taste you."

"Hmmm..." Your serious face twitches slightly with a smile, letting me know how much you are enjoying this. "Well, *if* you need it that badly. You're not done proving to me that you really deserve my dick in your mouth. But I'll deal with that later." And with that you signal me to unbuckle your belt with my suddenly poorly functioning fingers.

"Take it off, all the way," you instruct when my fumbling finishes and I've managed to disengage your buckle. I halt in my eager reach for your button fly, and resolutely pull your belt out carefully, loop by loop, until it rests freely in my sweaty hands.

"Set it over there," and you motion to a corner of your room. As I move to get up, you shove me back down. "I didn't say stand. Crawl."

"Yes, Sir. Sorry, Sir," I mumble, as heat travels up my body, flushing my face with embarrassment. I carefully place your folded belt in my mouth. I crawl to the corner, wincing with the pain of bony knees pressed to hard floor. After I return, you motion me to continue. *Finally,* I think. I grab the tops of your jeans and painstakingly begin unfastening the thick denim that covers your pale skin peeking out over your black harness. I pull your pants down and your thickly veined black rubber dick slowly emerges. This I move to cover inch by inch with my warm, wet mouth after its brief exposure to the cool night air.

Until you stop me, again. "Boy, aren't you forgetting something?" and you pull away from my mouth. Concealing a sigh of disappointment, I look in the direction of your finger-snap, to a stack of condoms resting on your nightstand.

"Of course, Sir, sorry, Sir." Again I painfully crawl off in the direction you've indicated. After grasping a single foil-wrapped, unlubed condom in my teeth, I come back to you and then open the package. I place the condom between my teeth and lips and then lean forward to push it down over you, slowly, carefully, so that my teeth don't tear the latex. When your dick is bulging in the taut rubber I pull back.

"Well..." your voice drawls out and then summons me to work in a staccato burst: "Get to it, you little cocksucker, you little fag. Show me how well you can suck dick!"

My desire, which I've tried to hold back all night as if I were a thirst-crazed animal, propels my mouth forward. I draw the tip of your cock into my mouth and then circle the rim with my tongue. Licking sideways down the shaft, I trace each vein until my mouth meets your harness. Then I travel down to the tip. I continue my slow savoring to the rhythm of your shallow breathing and then pull back. Your hands cradle the back of my head, fingers splayed, twitching with tense anticipation. Again I suck only the tip of you into my mouth, humming with satisfaction, and I linger, my tongue licking around and around, loving every second of serving you. Finally I plunge my mouth down your shaft, swallowing as much of your thick seven inches as I can, till your cockhead nudges the back of my throat. There I stay, pulling, feeding on you. Your fingers have stilled and now you grip me tightly and ride my mouth, grinding against my lips, your low moans telling me how much I am pleasing you. Finally your grip relaxes and I draw my swollen mouth off.

"Good boy," you say, smiling, causing the hairs on the back of my neck and arms to rise. "Now work up and down the side like you did before. Daddy really likes to watch you do that."

And so I do, teasing you with soft lip glides, moving into rough and sloppy licks, sliding my tongue down and around you, occasionally slipping and letting your dick slap me across the face. Then I concentrate on one side at a time before settling on your right and increasing my mouth's pressure in a desperate, fierce grip, bringing from you, "Oh yes, that's right, you little cocksucker."

Not stopping my work, I look up to see you gazing down at me, you absorbed in the vision of me mouthing your cock. *Right here*—I think—*this is the only place I want to be, on my knees, serving, sucking off my daddy*—and I am completely happy. Until you jerk your dick out of my mouth, leaving me to pitch forward, thrown off balance as any boy would be when separated from the source of his life's blood. As I steady myself, I can't contain a moan of disappointment, which soon trails off into a pitiful whimper.

"What do you say?" your harsh voice catches me.

"Thank-you, Daddy. Thank-you for letting me suck your dick."

"That's better. Don't worry, we're not done yet."

My heart lifts in expectation until you tuck your cock back into your pants. Then you lift me up by my chin and lead me to your bed, where you throw me down on my belly, and bind my hands.

"I'm not sure, but I think you enjoyed that just a little too much, so Daddy needs to punish you," you say.

First you use your hand, then you graduate to harder and meaner instruments as my ass pushes off the bed to meet your blows. Finally I am pulling and trying to twist away from you until I am pleading for you to stop. And you do for a bit, sending jolts through my body by running the tips of your fingers over my bruised and swollen ass. Your touch is soothing. My tense body slowly relaxes its tight hold on itself, and I let the bed fully support me.

"Just a little pink," you murmur disappointedly as your hands continue tracing my ass. "Well, we'll have to fix that." And with a hard slap you shock me back to you, making me squeal like a girl. You laugh and then say, "But first Daddy has to blindfold you." You tie a bandanna securely around my eyes and then push my head back into the bed.

As your finger strokes continue, I begin to relax again. Your hands travel up my ass toward my shoulders. Then you lower your mouth to the nape of my neck. Pressing your body down until I feel your entire weight, you kiss my neck, building into a teasing bite as your hands slide under my breasts and lightly cradle me. Instinctively my ass rises up to meet the bulge in your crotch, and you begin rubbing against me. Soon we are grinding together and I am begging you to fuck me.

You murmur into my ear, "You'd like that, wouldn't you, little boy, Daddy's big cock sliding in and out of you?"

"Mmhmm," I moan, pushing harder up into you, and then just as I remember that my hands are tied, you squeeze and twist my nipples hard and slam down on me. My whimper of frustration rolls into a wail with this new sensation, this pain, this taunting pleasure. But you force me with your body's weight to lie still, to absorb the twitches and shudders of my body.

"But we're not there yet," you whisper as you pull away. The cold of your room hits my bare skin, followed by a long pause and then the much harder hit of your hand. Again and again your palm comes down on me, warming, reddening my ass. Then I feel the meaner cut of a leather strap, causing me to yell and jerk with each blow. I lie tensely, expecting the next blow, and am surprised by the cold, lubed wetness of your latex-covered hand, prodding between my ass cheeks.

"Come on, boy. Open up now. Open up for me. This is where daddies get to go."

Your soothing words allow my muscles to go slack, and you slide a finger slowly into my ass. It hurts at first, but as you gently maneuver inside me, rubbing and lightly prodding, I find myself moving into your hand, helping you to go in further. But then you pull out, making me whimper, making me almost cry with disappointment.

"Shh, shh...you've been so good that Daddy has a little present for you."

I feel you push the smooth rubber of a medium-sized ass plug into me, and I moan with the sensation.

"Now can you hold that in for a while?"

Bleary, I whisper, "I think so, Daddy."

"Good," you say "Good boy."

Again you caress my ass with your hand and then with a harder, thinner instrument that I don't recognize. As you trace the stick-lick thing lightly on my ass and back you ask me, "Do you think you can take Daddy's cane now?"

And at the word "cane" my head pulls up "Wha...?"

"No, no," you push me back down. "Only a few times, and it would make your daddy so happy."

And of course, right there you've got me, because at this point I would do just about anything to make you happy. I nod and you push down on the plug in my ass, and then you wait.

The whistle of the cane cutting air seems to come long before the crack on my ass. At first the hit feels surprisingly mild and my body relaxes, for about a millisecond. Then a deep burn, the entire length of the cane trail, scores across my skin. I yell in shock, in pain, "Oh Daddy, no!" and this time I really mean it.

"Poor baby," you murmur sympathetically while you softly stroke my ass. And I believe you really mean it until I hear the second whistling cane descent. In the long moments that roll out between that sound and the hard clench of sharp pain that rides my body upon the cane's impact, I have forever to consider the coming blow, forever to shrink and try to pull away. But of course I can't, even in the involuntary spring of my body, because your shackles surge me down.

"Good boy." Your hand again touches my ass; the contrast of your soft skin after the hard whip gives me shivers and I whimper.

"Shhh. Such lovely marks on your ass. MmmHmm. But I think you need just one more."

"God, please no, Daddy. I can't take any more. It hurts too much," I plead.

"But I would really like you to take at least one more. Just for me. It would make me so happy. And I would reward you very well."

And once again, you've got me. "Okay," I raggedly breathe out. "Okay, one more, for you, just for you."

This time the cane seems to shriek through the heavy air of my waiting, waiting for you to mark me as yours. And the cane hits hard, forcing a rough groan out of my body as my senses begin to scream, giving into the noise in my head that finally escapes through my mouth in small cries. Now with my body quivering in pain, with barely suppressed sobs, I'm still concentrating on keeping the slippery ass plug inside of me.

You lower yourself onto me and hold me tightly. "Oh what a wonderful boy you've been," you whisper in my ear. And we stay that way for a few minutes while I calm down. Finally you pull away. Next you roughly push my legs apart with your knee, making the ass plug's position even more precarious. I cling to it like the small bit of hope I've been hoarding all night, like forbidden candy, that you still might actually fuck me. "Please, please, Daddy, fuck me. I've tried to be so good."

I hear the snap of a fresh condom and you say, "Well, yes, I think you've been very good." You push the plug farther inside of me with a gloved hand and then you guide your big cock between my splayed legs. Rubbing the head against my cunt lips you taunt me slowly. Then in one movement you push your way in until you are buried deep inside my cunt. Grasping my hips, you begin to stroke in and out, building tempo until you are pounding, slamming into me, and my body is rising and pushing into each stroke.

"Daddy-takes-good-care-of-you-doesn't-he?" You grunt each word between strokes.

"God, yes. Yes you do, Daddy." I answer as I move my cunt harder over your cock and my excitement builds.

"Daddy?"

"Yes?"

"Can I please touch my clit?"

You answer by untying my right hand, which I quickly move between my legs. For the first time that night, I really know how wet and swollen I am as I find my engorged clit and I begin rubbing it, deliberate and hard. You slow to match my pace, your cock stroking, grinding inside me purposefully and your belly keeping the plug in place. Until it is too much for me and there is only one conclusion—I hope. So I ask, "Daddy, can I come please?" Near-panic permeates my words as I am half expecting you to say no, so used to the teasing, the buildup, which

I now know is half, or more than half, of everything here.

For a long moment you cease your movement and my breath catches in my throat as we seem to hover over the "no" that we both know is coming. Then you give me another stroke, your cock burning into my cunt, and then another and another, until I can't hold back anymore. Finally, when I am moaning and crying out, you release me by saying, "Yes, boy, you can come." And I do, all over myself, all over my beginnings, my starting place, my point of conception, all over my daddy's relentless, driving cock.

Cleo's Gone

Gwendolyn Bikis

I.

I'm just getting ready to wash my white school blouse in the bathroom sink when the phone rings.

"Baby sister. What's shakin'?" It's Marla, calling from Charlotte. From the Girls' Club, no doubt, she's talking so street-like.

"Nuthin' doin," I reply. "You comin' home this weekend?"

"I just might. But that sure ain't the reason I'm calling. I just got a call, long distance—collect. From Cleo."

I feel my breath leave me. Already I am certain this isn't going to be real good.

"She asked me to send her some math books." A pause. "Tammy? She called me from the women's prison? They've already moved her from the jail. She's 'up against a li'l charge' is all she'll tell me. And she's not sounding too proud of whatever it is she's been charged with *this* time. This time, sounds like it's gon' stick."

I can see the loose little shrug that Cleo'd give, acting cool and shucking, all the way into...into prison, this time. Before it had just been lock-up, "diddly little county time," Cleo called it, bragging about it in that way that people will about their trouble when it's the only thing they have.

Marla sighs into the phone. "Cleo's life has done went all to hell and pieces, exactly how she wanted it to go. I'm not sure if knowing where she's at is any much better than wondering if she's dead." She lets out a flat, not-happy laugh.

"Aah, Marla—" is all I can say.

Cleo's gone; gone for sure now.

II.

Cleo was Marla's Little Sister, whom Marla had adopted soon as I'd gone off to college. I think I was supposed to be jealous that Marla had a substitute, but I was the one who ended up getting the last laugh.

I remember the first time I saw her play, saw her legs and arms as long as licorice sticks, so whip-like she nipped the ball out the other players' fingers, snapped and plucked the rebounds before they hit the backboard, jumped so quick it seemed there were springs in her knees. Cleo is a li'l bit darker than me and built just wiry, all tight and smooth at once. Cleo *moved* like silk sliding through water.

Cleo...I can see you with your sleek legs flying, your lanky muscles stretching tight, the stripes around your socks, around the hems of your red-silk real-tight basketball shorts...

Her jump shots were so smooth she could have been diving up through water, and watching her make them put me in the shivers, as though she were sliding, silkenly, all along the most secret of my places. She'd bounce and flick that ball around a helpless tangle of legs and arms that hopelessly tried to stop her. One time, she dribbled the ball right out of some chick's fingers, then darting and springing around her, bounced the ball—I swear—right through the girl's out-spread legs, catching it off the bounce before her opponent even had the chance to *think* of turning around.

"Cleo's Back," said the front of her favorite black sweatshirt, in bright pink letters. "Cleo's Gone," said the other side. Sometimes, by the time you figured out where Cleo was back *from,* she'd already be long gone. "Slick" was the word she chose to describe herself, because like everyone with the player's personality, Cleo had two sides: street side and court side. On the court, Cleo wore her lucky black-canvas hightops; but coming in off the street, she wore new suede or leather tennis, and she cussed if someone so much as scuffed them and fussed when Marla asked her where she'd gotten them from.

"Because she knew I was actually asking her where did she get the wherewithall to get them from."

Everybody knew that Cleo had absolutely no visible means, other than hanging 'round the littered, rotten-smelling courtyard of the M C Morningside Homes, hanging out supposedly empty-handed.

"But you never can tell what-all I got in my socks, or in my secret pockets," Cleo bragged.

Man oh man, when I think of how gone I was over that girl...from the beginning of that summer I was visiting Marla, managing her team, until the August day she made me leave, I had one hopeless schoolgirl crush. I'd be sitting on the sidelines making like my own Girls' Club cheerlead-ing squad, until everybody started to see who I was really cheering for. And the thing about it was, Cleo didn't need more cheering.

"F that 'everybody's a star' stuff," she'd say, not saying the full curse word because Marla had forbidden her to swear. "I'm the only star on this team." And she'd thump her ball a couple times off the locker room bench, as if to punch the point home.

After she won her Most Valuable Player trophy, every kid on the block wanted Cleo's autograph. I remember her standing smiling in a mob of kids, her face still shining with sweat, the top of her royal-red jacket snapped closed over her shoulders, signing scrap after scrap of paper. "Good luck. Signed C.L."; "Happy baskets, signed Cleo." Even though she couldn't write too well, and funny as the ink pen looked, bobbling loosely in her fingers, she grinned through every minute of it.

"That might be the only time you'll see Cleo happy to be holding a pen," Marla grumbled. Sometimes she'd get so discouraged with her other Little Sister.

Like anyone with an awkward name, Cleo always had plenty of nick-names: C.L., Likorish, Cleo T., Cool Cleo—all of them hiding the name of—Cleotha. Cleo hated Cleotha, hated it with a red-eyed passion, hated it like she hated being stepped on. Cleotha reminded her of a "dumpy country girl with glasses," a girl who'd be afraid of someone like Cleo, so afraid she'd give up all her milk-and-candy money, let herself be kissed, then offer over her sandwich.

"I beat plenty kids up for food when I was a child," Cleo bragged. "I just had to, they was being so greedy. It ain't *polite* to eat in front of folks who ain't got. It ain't right, so I had to start on them." Cleo rubbed her fist.

"I would have given you some," I answered.

"You would have given me *all,* baby." She smiled then, showing off the squareness of her chin.

Cleo is an Aries, like me: sometimes we're so selfish, we don't even know we're being it. Or so Marla says—but I believe that Cleo's a whole lot worse, a lot more selfish, than me. If it was me, I'd think twice about kissing someone, especially some other girl—even more, some other girl who, most likely, would not want it. After she picked me, and after she kissed me, she told me this:

"I knew you'd like it, once I did it, so I just went ahead and did." And that smile again—flashing, then closing, like the quick white glint of a pocket knife.

Cleo thought she was smooth, but she sure had one real quick atti-tude. Let someone step on her toes wrong, even in a basketball game, for goodness' sake, and Cleo'd go off. I remember tears in her eyes, she'd be so hurt that someone had made her so red-hot mad. I remember how she got, cutting her eyes and snarling 'bout "someone" saying this or doing that. I recall a time that "someone" had draped Cleo's jacket over their own "stinkin', sweatin' shoulders." By pure mistake, thinking the jacket was their own, but you sure couldn't tell Cleo that, just like you couldn't tell her that this wasn't the Training School, where everyone just naturally stole from *her,* the youngest and the skinniest of all.

That's how I knew that Cleo really thought of me as "her" girl: the game when she let me wear her jacket for a whole entire two quarters. After that game, after everyone was gone, the showers dripping off and me innocently picking up the dirty towels, Cleo backed me up against the lockers, and her mouth was spicy with the taste of Good 'n Plenty. I knew, that day, that it was just a matter of time before I'd be back on the bus toward home, back toward everything that was boring to me.

III.

Cleo never gave me flowers, never said she cared for me, and always asked for money—which sometimes she would get—so why'd I ever love her? It was all about her beauty, the way that she would press her hands all along her long, strong body and grin at me.

"Sometimes I makes sweet love to my own self," she would say.

Not too many people's darker than I am, and Cleo's one of them. What does it mean to put your hand beside someone's and see how close its color matches yours, even more than your own sister's does? What does it mean to know this color, so beautiful, chose your color out of knowledge of its beauty?

By the end of August, when Marla finally called Mama to let her know that I was on my way back home, by that hot and steamy time, I'd heard the threat one hundred thousand times:

"Im'a send you back down home, Tamara."

The first time I heard it was the July night I came in drowsy, hungry, and smelling like burnt rope. Me and Cleo had smoked weed, sneaked it back behind the Homes where they backed up on a park that really was kind of piss-stinky. Though naturally I didn't say as much, not wanting to be called a "sissy country girl."

"I know that you afraid to go with me and get sky-high," she said to lure me, smiling in her shark-like way. Didn't she know it though? Don't nobody tell Tamara what she's afraid to do.

That day, she was wearing black suede tennis shoes, shorts, and pulled-tight knee socks. And carrying her cap, I'm sure so I could see how neat her hair lay, all newly dressed and styled, shaved short around her ears and back along her hairline. And Lordy, she was smelling so good to me, like sweet grease and barber-shop powder, she smelled good enough to be eaten; and she surely knew it too.

We settled in the evening sun beside the worn-out courts. Cleo reached inside the lining of her cap and held up a little hand-rolled cigarette. She stretched, and then she yawned so wide I could see the whole way up inside her mouth.

"Act as though you got some manners," I almost let my sister's words pass through my own two lips. Cleo liked to stretch and scratch, to pick her teeth in public—with her fingernail yet—liked to belch and never say excuse me. Cleo was the kind of child that Mama would feel sorry for, would shake her head and softly suck her teeth over.

"Think I got some matches." She was searching through her pants pockets—though I couldn't see, with those jeans tight as they were, how she could've fit a thing much thicker than a folded piece of paper into those pockets.

"Look inside you jacket, Cleo," I suggested. The first time I'd seen Cleo high, she couldn't do nothing but laugh and dance and suck the popsicles she'd gotten me to buy for her. When she wasn't high, Cleo made me tense and flushed every time she touched herself. Now she stroked one hand along her pants front, while groping through her jacket pocket with her other hand, and it made my neck tingle. It made me curious, how could one of Cleo's hands be scrabbling even as the other one so casually, so smoothly, was taking care of yet another kind of business? Was it true a person could be born with hands belonging to a criminal? Secretly, I shivered.

"Here it go," she said, pulling out a book of matches. "You ready?" She grinned, whipping that weed cigarette from behind her ear and holding it so I could see it.

"I am a big girl now, for your information," I said out loud, to whom I wasn't sure.

Cleo raised her eyebrow, struck the match, and grinned her sharp-toothed grin. "What you gonna do, babe, when I—" but she'd stopped to breathe smoke in, pulling wisps of it into her nostrils.

When you do what, Cleo? Like you the one invented the idea of getting next to me? I thought as I grinned right back. Now she was handing it to me, it was smoking, and she was grinning back at me grinning back at her.

I reached out for the cigarette and put it to my lips and drew it in, keeping both my eyes closed tight. I drew it in and—coughed and heaved, but somehow kept my lips together tight enough to keep the smoke inside. Even I knew that was what you had to do. When I opened my eyes, still holding my breath, the world outside still looked the same. Somehow I had thought it wouldn't.

"You ain't high yet, baby sis," Cleo said, watching me while I looked around and waited. I guess I ain't, I thought, but how'm I gon' know it when...when suddenly I felt it—like something pulling out away from me, slow-motion out from under me. And all this heat, this depth and color rushing in at me.

"Wo-ow," I heard myself sigh. In a way, my own sounds I made, my own thoughts I had, seemed like something I was hearing from outside myself. And the scene I was in seemed more like something I was looking at. It was like another depth to my perception.

"You like this, babe?" Naturally I thought she was talking 'bout the weed, until I looked down at her long hand and her longer fingers creeping all along my thigh. "Poppety pop," she said, arching an eyebrow. "Poppety pop my finger pop."

"Mmmm," I said.

Cleo's hand was moving, quivering on me. "You untouched, baby sis?" she asked.

What difference could it make to her? I mean, God knew she wasn't.

"Sam," was what I said. Funny, I had gotten through the summer without so much as thinking about that ex-man of mine, and here I'd gone and mentioned him. At a very inconvenient moment too.

She snatched back as though my leg had stuck her with a splinter. "Who the hell is *Sam?*"

"Oh," I waved my hand to show how bored I was with this topic. "This man I used to know." Used to. Know. I didn't like to lie like that.

"You know that man good as I know Cynamon?" Cleo asked. "Know that man all the ways I be knowin' her?"

Cynamon? Was I hearing right? Cynamon was the Lady Panthers' center, who had a twitchy booty and not a whole lot more. What-all could anyone *find* to know about somebody like Cynamon? Cynamon painted her nails bright orange and looked at stories on TV, those times she wasn't making up no even-more-stupid stories of her own about the boys she knew, away now in the army or sometimes the Marines, and the presents they bought or were going to buy for her. Not that I ever laid my eyes on present one:

"My baby Wally go' buy me a microwave and eelskin shoes and satin underthings."

Now who was going to believe that, and who was going to care enough to tell her she was clear and plain a liar?

"Cynamon?" I wanted to know what Cleo knew about girls, every little bit of it, but I didn't care to hear about Cynamon. "She likes boys, Cleo."

Cleo grinned. "Not no mo' she don't. Least not since I turnt her out, so's to speak."

Turnt her out? I never had understood just what "turnt out" meant, but I'd never had known how to ask without seeming too sweet and churched and babyish.

"How'd you do that, Cleo?" I heard myself ask, despite the fact of it including Cynamon.

Cleo tap-rubbed at my leg. "Turnt her inside out, I mean. Made her river run the uphill way." Cleo moved in a li'l bit closer to me. Even with my eyes closed I could feel her, hear her jacket leather squeaking while she shifted.

"You wantin' me tell you 'bout it, sis, or you wantin' me to show you?"

"Mmm, tell me first." Eyes closed, I leaned back all ready to be told. I was feeling very lazy, floating away out in the middle of a drowsy, sleepy sea.

"Then show me too," I actually said. I pictured me and Cleo, floating arm in arm up to the sky on a *natural* high.

"Yeah..." Cleo's voice had deepened. "Yeah—I like to ease on back and watch whiles I be poppin' 'um, watch 'em knot their brows like they in pain, then smile as though they ain't, and I like to hear 'em grunt and cry and moan an' squeak and beg like how the ladies do once you got them goin' good, got 'em good and sweet and greezed."

Ooh my goodness, that was nasty, nastier than I'd ever heard her be. What would Marla say and do? I couldn't exactly see Cleo lying slapped-down on her back, but I couldn't see Marla doing anything less.

"Know how I picked that fist girl I ever really wanted?" Cleo asked.

"Who was that, Cleo?" I noticed I had caught my breath, the way I do whenever I feel jealous. Me, having to be jealous of a simple-face like Cynamon.

"What I mean, li'l sis, is that usually they's the ones be wantin' me, and I just goes along just for the ride, so's to speak."

"Just for the ride?" Was it the weed, or was it something else that was making my arms and legs feel so limp and weak and warm? And making me sound so very young and stupid?

"Mm—mmm tha's right. Mmm...hmm. But you want to know how I picked that first girl I ever really wanted?"

"How?" I obliged by asking. How could a person tell, ever, what it was they really wanted?

"You mean, how'd I *find* that girl I wanted? That's the question that I'm tryin' to answer you with, now. If I went ahead and answered it, I might be tellin' you about this party I had went to, deep down in the East Bee-mo' jungle, way way late at night, so late it was gettin' on toward early. That blue lightbulb had been burnin' for a good long while by the time Cool Cleo finally got there.

"So then I walks right in, real sharp, wid my cap politely in my hands 'cause I know it's go' be ladies there—I walks on in, and ooh wee, what right off do I see?"

I opened my eyes, and I leaned so far forward, I almost fell. I propped myself on both my hands. "What did you see, Cleo?"

"I saw one whole line of ladies, baby sister, all preening and a-strolling that old hip-grind booty-shake they be usin' on the street, and all of it is just for me, Cool Cleo.

"Then up to me, comes a lay-dee," Cleo sang it. "This long-haired light-skin lady in a evening gown with some silvery tinselish fringe along its front come strolling up to me, hip-grinding booty-shaking right up to me, and ask me would I like a glass of wine. Which you already know, Cleo isn't go' refuse.

"So I sits there sippin'—the lady done provided me a seat—and lookin' all these ladies over, all of which is wantin' me, waitin' just to do whatever I be wantin' them to do for me, when I sees this one in back?"

"Uh huh?" I nodded with my eyes closed, thinking all of this was sounding too wild even for a life like Cleo's.

"This one look quiet, like she's hiding an' surprised to find herself in this late-night doing, and she's wondering why has she been invited? I mean, this one definitely ain't no party lady, so why she been invited here? Look to me as though she's thinking that, hanging back there in the corner lookin' all so quiet and so sweet.

"Then up to me, comes the lady," Cleo sang again. "The lady in the evenin' gown? She seen my glass is drunk down to its dregs. So then she start to po' some mo' of that plum wine, and then she lean down toward my ear, and then she sing to me:

" 'Spill that wine, take that girl—' "

"Oh, Cleo," I play-slapped at her arm. "That is that *song,* Cleo." That song I should have recognized, because it had been all over the radio a couple summers before.

Cleo laughed, but then went on. "But you wan' know how I decided which girl it was that I was gon' take? I decided when that sweet girl been hiding in the back was brought up to me by the lady in the evening gown. That sweet young thang is looking giggly, like she likes me so she gots to cover it with silliness. An' there she goes, giggling even harder when I lean in toward her to touch them thick soft lips with mines. And I know, soon as I am kissing her, I know it then fo' sho': this the one. This the girl that I been wanting, this dark-skinned soft and chubby one with the real sweet features and the cute print skirts and li'l red Keds and the oh-so-easy feelings I can see inside of, right this living minute. I can see that she the one, once I gits her in the bed, the one gon' scream an' cry more happier than she ever done in church. Because the facts is that she ain't yet had real lovin'. Ain't had *my* real lovin'."

I felt so naked, I felt X-rayed. Embarrassment had never before felt so exciting to me. Not before right now.

"So now I'm thinking I'ma take that girl," Cleo said, and then she took me. With my eyes closed and my head all weed-smoke dizzy, Cleo took and hugged and kissed my breath away. 'Cept for that tiny squeak I loosed.

That was the real beginning, that first long tight and sliding full-tongue kiss that I gave back to her. That was the real beginning of my realizing *how* I was much more than someone else's little sister. And in those rapturous high moments I couldn't care at all about whatever people might think of to call me.

All the ways and why of how we kissed: We kissed one time so deep, just because it felt so good, that afterward, still dizzy, as I was dazedly signing on a form, I looked down at my hand, and I saw that I had misspelt my own name. Badly, in two places. We kissed one time so sweet, just because it tasted good, sneaked little dabs of lip sugar back behind the gym bleachers, so sweet that I forgot to stop, and we almost got caught by watchdog Coach Alberta.

"What y'all doin' back up in there? Poppin' popcorn maybe?"

We kissed so juicy, so flavor-full for days, sneaked inside the laundry room because the sneaking was so fun. I remember still the way her lips would feel. Luckily, because it is most likely I will never feel those lips on mine again.

IV.

I'd went over to the Morningside to look for her, that last-ever morning I got to spend with her.

"You have exactly twenty minutes to go and say good-bye to her," Marla had said, and tapped her wristwatch, and I knew she thought she was being fair to give me that.

I didn't have to look too far, because Cleo had been waiting for me in the stairwell, sitting on a step with her ball in her hand.

"Hi babysis."

She stood and flicked her leg muscles. And she smiled, her tongue pressed teasingly to the gap between her two front teeth.

"Hey Cleo," I said, in a voice that was thick with all my misery.

"Ah, don't be taking it that way." She reached for my hand, and *pulled* me toward her. Her ball had dribbled away into a corner.

"Just 'cause big sis don't want you hanging out with big old bad-ass me no more."

"I couldn't give a care what Marla wants," I decided out loud. Now what did I do that for, I remember thinking, because what Cleo did then was press her bare lanky leg into my—you know. My breath froze: what was she *doing* to me? I'd fallen helplessly into the shivers.

Her tongue moved on my lips, and she pressed me closer and moved her kissings to my cheek, my chin, all down my neck. All I could do was close my eyes and try real hard not to make a noise. Where in the world was Marla when I needed her?

"You have such a long, long neck," she was crooning, and what did I do but smile, and stretch it longer for more kisses? Both her hands were holding tight to my behind, so that I couldn't get away. I reached for her own round, high-riding...

"Hey girl!" And she pulled back from me, so sudden-like she scared me, and slapped my wrists away.

"What, Cleo?" I almost felt like crying.

"Le's go upstairs," she whispered hotly in my ear, with her hands holding mine behind me.

Feeling ashamed and tough and sneaky, I crept up the four flights right behind her.

"Ssh," Cleo put her finger to her mouth as she quietly opened her apartment's door, "Auntie-dear is sleeping."

We slipped inside, past a darkened living-kitchenette, on into Cleo's bedroom. Where she latched the door. I looked around, a little desperately, because there certainly wasn't much in that little bedroom to offer distraction, nor even any conversation: just a very neat bureau with her trophy on it, a poster of a long, tall player with his arm arched ready to sink a basket, and a made-up bed with her tennis shoes—all eight pairs—all neatly lined up under it. Cleo grinned, and was of course noticing just where I was looking.

"I'll be your good girl if you'll put your shoes underneath my bed," she sang. She was leading me right to it, sliding her hand along her pillow. "I want to rub your tummy till your cherry turns bright red." By now her hand crawled all up under my blouse, her fingers gently pinching the sweet meat of my belly, before creeping down toward my zipper.

Next I know, I was on my back, barefooted, without my skirt, with Cleo's fingers inching up my thigh, up close to my...

M-A-ARLA, I wanted to yell. Why didn't I?

She began massaging me down there, with the strong, commanding palm of her hand, the whole while singing in my ear: "Won't your sister be disgusted, when she see your cherry busted?" I might've tried to reply, or wanted to wiggle away, but I couldn't hardly, because she was holding me down and covering my mouth with her lips, her kiss; and one of her long, sleek legs was sliding up between mine, so that my belly began to shake. Even harder, when she slipped her finger under my panties. "Take yo' drawers off, sugar babe?"

Well, what could I do? I let her take my panties off. "Ride me baby," she begged me, her breath hot, almost sobbing. "Wrap 'em all around me." Then she's sliding and gliding all over me, until I catch her rhythm deep down inside my middle, all through my shivering secret places.

"Oooh." My eyes popped open when she put her fingers there, pumping them in and out as I felt myself foam like clabber and tighten around her. And she's pulling me up tight, churning in and out until my hips rock the bed so hard, so steady, that its springs begin to sing. Cleo's laughing, while I thrash and bite the pillow; she's laughing and kissing me rashly round my face. "You really like that, huh baby huh?" I'm swooning, seeing nothing but velvet wings, brushing across the midnight sky with their black-silk tips. I can't even moan, she's got my mouth so covered, my lips and tongue so tightly wrapped and pressed in hers.

"Oh Tammy, that's some sweet—" and she used that "p" word, that nasty sticky-sweet word. Evil, coming from a street curb, but here just soft and tender, the way I'd never heard it. I groaned, and pulled myself up tighter.

"CLEO!" Cleo's auntie's voice, just the other side of the door. Cleo's hand came away from me so fast I collapsed back onto the bed.

"Ma'am?"

"It's someone here to see you."

She stood up, wiped her fingers on her bedspread. "We'd best get you dressed, babysis. It's probably big sis now."

So I right quick threw my clothes on.

It was just like Marla, always right on time, but never coming right just when I wanted her. Marla had her hand propped up on her hip, and her foot tapped impatient time while I asked Cleo's aunt for an ink pen and paper so I could at least get Cleo's address.

"I'll write," I promised Cleo's laughing eyes, and hugged her oh-so-stiffly.

"Time to go, Tammy," was all that Marla said, and I could tell by the tightness of her lips, and the way she wouldn't even look at Cleo, or my very wrinkled blouse, that she knew.

Outside, I felt obliged to explain: "We was just—"

"Tamara, you know, I ain't even gon' ask." I could tell exactly how upset she was, by her grammar slippage.

"It wasn't anything, Marla."

"I am sure it wasn't. I am sure she just led you up there, like Mary had a little innocent lamb."

And you know, to this day that is probably what Marla is *still* telling herself.

I throbbed the whole ride home, wriggling restlessly in my bus seat just at the thought of Cleo's fingers there inside me. Damn Marla damn, I swore, squirming hooked through the middle on a velvet rope. I'd've sworn even harder if I had thought that'd be the very last time I'd ever see Cleo. A couple months after Marla sent me away, Cleo disappeared anyway; and nobody Marla knew was telling where to.

here

Renita Lynet Martin

call me james brown while i dance
on the cum-stained floor of your
steamy juke joint   and let these legs be
eyes seeing rhythms/dancing
in shades of

        1

      maroon

          2

        black

             3

           pulpy

                4

              earth green

5 6 7 8 toes already in the water
and i'm still burning up
the floor and burning up and
burning up like when the sage stick
becomes fire
burning until your joint is smudged
and there is nothing else.   but the smoke of the rhythm of the color...

until there is nothing
else but us/here/in this
charred slow drag called us/here.

fruit song

Renita Lynet Martin

i had to ask
where she was from
'cause she talked like
my mama when she said

"i don't like nothin' you got
to thump to see if it's ripe
give me a plum i can roll around
in my fingers i can work with that"

but my mama ain't never wore
no baseball cap turned back and
her jeans don't come down around
her waist which ain't
at all as fine as country girls'

so while i went to the grocery
store for one thing i stayed
for this new fruit-
toting mama in the tank top
as rugged as the watermelon
she did not want

and while i went to the grocery
store for one thing
i had to ask where she was
goin' could i be the plum
in those fingers till her basket
was full

Sherry

Jane Perkins

Sherry takes me to the city for shopping, movies, museums, and plays. I already saw *Don't Bother Me, I Can't Cope, The Fantasticks,* and *The New York Experience.* We drive there in her white Mercedes. The seats are leather, the color of pumpkins. I rub my cheek against them. I pretend they are mine and not just hers. People look at us like we're something special when we're driving in this car. One day I will ask her to teach me how to drive it and maybe she'll let me take it out my own self.

Sherry travels during the week, so I stay here by myself and watch TV. Sometimes I wonder what the kids are doing in school, and I feel a little lonely even though I didn't have friends there. I did like learning things. You can learn from TV too, but it's not the same. I suppose I could get a job, but I'm so tired all the time that I'm afraid I'll fall asleep at work or something. Unless I could get a job as a mattress tester, like Li'l Abner. Sometimes I think about working at those topless bars where businessmen go at lunch, but they don't take girls with flabby bellies like mine. If I was nursing they say the flab would go right away, but you can't nurse a baby you don't have any more so that's that.

I keep this place very clean so Sherry will know I'm not a bum. The dishes are always washed carefully and put away, and I wipe off the sink until it shines. I dust the paperweights. Sherry has them on the glass coffee table in the living room and on the desk in her office. Thick, perfect glass globes with iridescent swirls inside, like captured stardust. I get the coffee table so clean there is no lint or particles on it, and then I place the paperweights down carefully. I can make things sparkle.

She has an oriental rug—green, gold, black, and white. When you vacuum it the colors come out richer. After I do my chores I lie on the green velveteen couch in the clean room and I watch TV. Everything feels just fine except for one thing. The throwing up has come back. I thought it had stopped. When I was pregnant, after the morning sickness went away, I didn't ever want to throw up again. It's not like I do it every day—that's one good thing—but when I get the urge nothing can stop me. I guess you just get bored after watching so many soaps and reruns so you think about eating. It does make the day go. You wake up and watch the morning shows and think about having ice cream for breakfast. Then you're sunk. Once you start, that's it for the day. You think of how fat you'll get after you eat it and then you remember that you can have as much as you want and then throw it up and you'll have it both ways. After you throw up you get really tired so you sleep from about five till eight, then you get up for more TV and watch it till eleven or twelve. Then you go to bed. You know this isn't normal but it makes perfect sense at the time.

Sherry doesn't know I do this. She doesn't know much about me, really. It's amazing that she lets me stay here. She doesn't know about the baby, or about running away. She thinks I'm taking a year off of high school to decide what I want to do with my life. She doesn't pry much. I guess I'll tell her when I'm ready, if I'm ever ready.

She usually comes home on Thursday and so we spend Friday together. I don't throw up when she's here. She gets in late; I wait up for her. I have cookies and milk waiting. She likes that. She says she's grateful for me.

We sleep in her bed, a queen size. It has satin sheets. They make you feel like you're under water. When she's not here I sleep on the couch with the TV on.

I don't let her touch me down there, but she can touch me every-place else. I'm the one who touches her down there. She comes really easy. I haven't come yet with another person, only by myself. I wonder what I would do if it happened. Would I scream or something stupid like that? I hope I wouldn't say "Oh, yes." I wouldn't let myself make any noise at all.

When we go to the city we go out to eat. We make sure to find a place with tablecloths so we can touch under the table. The waiter will be taking our order and I'll have my hand on her leg, under her skirt. I bend down and pretend to look for something, and while she orders for us I go right between her legs. Her thighs are soft as baby's skin. I touch her panties and feel her getting wet already. I like this very much. I see her try to keep a still face and I get to wanting her so much I don't know what to do with myself. After the waiter leaves she lets out her breath real slow.

"You're bad," she says. "Bad, bad, bad. You've got me all worked up. What are you going to do now?"

"I could finish you off," I say.

"You wouldn't dare," she says.

"Oh, wouldn't I?" I say. I sense that this is how she wants me to be.

I push my chair closer to hers so that I won't have to bend to get to her pussy. My finger goes under the elastic of her panties and into her labia. She's very slippery. All I need to do is move my finger back and forth very gently over her clitoris and she jerks the tiniest bit in her seat. She lets out a little cough and I feel her pulsing and getting wetter.

She whispers to me, "Oh, baby, now you've done it...you've finished me off without hardly trying. You're magic." I start to take my finger away and she says, "Leave it." I tell her I have to go to the bathroom and I take it out, careful to secretly wipe my finger on the tablecloth before I get up.

Each time I take a step I feel like my own clit swells up more. The wet has made me sting; I'm still raw from the baby.

In the stall I finish my own self off. It doesn't take long. If there's someone in the next stall I come even quicker. When I come I clear my throat. I leave as much wet as I can so I'll feel it all night. I do not wash my hands when I leave the washroom.

I come back to the table and Sherry looks at me like she loves me, like I'm the only one who can make her feel this good. I want her to think that.

"I missed you," she says.

"I missed you too," I say.

This night we're going to see *Oklahoma*. We have seats in the center, a few rows back. We will have to behave ourselves because we are exposed.

She leans over to me and says, "You make me feel alive."

I wish I knew what you meant, I think.

Clash of the Titans

Karlyn Lotney

She gave up a Saturday night to come see me. Now, this may seem like no big deal, but when you are the featured dancer at San Francisco's most expensive "gentleman's club," and fucking yourself in front of German tourists who use a flashlight to afford themselves an intimate view of your vulva nets you a thousand bucks a show, Saturday night is, indeed, a big deal. She called to inform me that she was writing a paper detailing the status of women in Bolivian culture, and that she was coming over within the hour for my assistance.

"Be prepared," she commanded softly.

She was my first femme top.

Taking her directive to heart, I busied myself around the apartment, gearing up for my traditional last-minute a-trick-is-coming-over m.o., throwing dirty clothes and papers into the closet, and collecting the dishes that had gathered since the last time we'd had sex. Luckily, I live in the Castro, where finding a decent florist is easier than locating a Frisch's Big Boy in the Midwest. I rushed out to the fanciest shop in the neighborhood and brought home a lovely arrangement of orange and fuchsia Gerber daisies, four perfect irises, and an enormous Cala lily. I know how to buy flowers for a femme.

Once I'd placed the flowers artfully on my desk, I fired up my Macintosh IIsi and found a generic entry on Bolivia in the Random House Encyclopedia software that came with my computer. I pulled a book on writing critical papers from the shelf and set it next to a pad of paper by the computer. The flowers were placed far enough from the pad to keep from being a nuisance, yet close enough to inspire loftiness in her thoughts. I found the classical station and turned the music down to a whisper, leaving just enough volume to produce an air of vague intellectualism in my little basement flat. Finally, I sat down on the couch and arranged myself in a casual pose, as though I always lounged about my pristine living room, Cala lilies draped overhead, computer at the ready, Mozart playing in the background, incidentally poised to entertain the occasional errant stripper cum scholar who might randomly drop by my home. She was, after all, my first femme top.

The doorbell rang, and when I answered it, my carefully constructed composure went right over the doorstep she was gracing. She stood there, nothing less than an impossibly perfect vision in BeBe, size two. Now, BeBe is the kind of clothier whose stock rises and falls with the relative success of flawless, high-priced call-girls everywhere, and she basically wore BeBe or nothing at all. In either state, BeBe-bedecked or nude, she would produce an effect in anyone with a milliliter of either estrogen or testosterone—with something akin to the force that sent Frankie Avalon reeling when the Gina Lolabrigida wannabe did her famous hip swing. *She was fine.* And despite my careful ministrations, I was made powerless whenever she entered a room.

"May I come in?" she said, amused by my hormonal subjugation.

"Oh, sure; *please,* uh, by all means. You look, well, really amazing. Uh, I've been checking out information about Bolivia on my computer, and there really isn't much there, I'm afraid. You probably have all the facts you need, though, I suppose. Oh, by the way, I have some oranges in the fridge if you're hungry." She snickered almost imperceptibly and looked up at me with that same amused smile; this time it reflected the ridiculousness of my efforts to divert her attention from the fool butch blankness that was holding me hostage. She stared into my eyes, let her coat drop to the floor, and revealed the ebullient, lycra-covered lines that defined her perfect porn star body.

She cut a swath through my flat like Moses parting the Red Sea, and made me feel like a man: all big and dumb and panting. I felt my internal butch cock harden and start its invisible levitation, and the part of my brain that concerns itself with floral arrangements, oranges, and perfect living rooms fell away. Another part took over, the part that found its genesis in my father's collection of late sixties' issues of *Playboy,* benches two-ten, and answers to "Daddy."

"I'm not hungry," she said as she swept into the hall and positioned herself against the wall opposite me, a few inches away from my body.

I must have been giving her one of those steely, hardass stares that appear inadvertently on my face after Jimmy Stewart has vacated my psyche and porn legend John Holmes has taken his place, because she broke out of her femme top superiority stance long enough to angle her hips up slightly, look at me coquettishly, measure the effect of her proximity on me, and ask, "Are you hungry, baby?"

My phantom dick rose further in response to the sound of her voice and the movement of her hips and bridged the narrowing gap between us. My breathing thickened as my desire lodged itself in my fingertips; my every gesture was sexual. I leaned into her and put my hands, throbbing and rough, on her waist; its taut, shimmery tininess made them feel enormous and iron strong. I encompassed her rib cage in them and moved them slowly down the length of her torso. From there, I reached down quickly to the hem of her dress and exposed her completely; one swift movement upward and she was bare. I returned my hands to her waist and spread my thumbs out from her stomach up to the nipples of her unbelievable 34Ds, kicked her legs apart, and lifted her up against the wall as she opened her legs and arms around me. I pulled her head back by her long, thick hair with one hand and, with the other, pressed my palm into the vulnerability of her throat as I kissed her violently.

I was her first butch top.

I lifted her up against the wall and spread her legs so that they rested on my shoulders. I held her ass up by my fingertips so that her snatch was about an inch and a half away from my face. It was smooth shaven, firm, and tight, and just thinking about how it would taste gave me a boner that could rip through my 501s. Her cunt smelled like refined debauchery, and her pussy lips and clit hood were like perfumed velvet, brushing against my forehead, eyelids, and nose.

I moved the heat radiating from her with my tongue, and I came excruciatingly close to her lips without actually touching them. She tried to maintain her composure—she couldn't do anything that might be construed as begging. My teasing was making her crazy though, and she writhed around my neck and tried to rub her box on my rough, warm mouth. I had moved us both to pain with waiting; her body was shaking in front of me, and the promise of that cunt moved me to a violence that we both needed. I threw her ass back into the wall and spread her so hard that both her knees hit the plaster. Finally, she spread her swollen clit and come-slicked lips in front of me, grabbed the muscles in my shoulders, moved farther into me, and muttered anxiously, "Oh, Jesus, suck it, baby."

She had made an offering of herself, despite her best intentions.

"You wanna be Daddy's hole, baby? You make me so hard, bitch, I could just split your cunt wide open with my big dick."

She smiled coyly and said: "Now, is that any way to talk to a teenager, Karlyn?"

Now, she was a seasoned nineteen, to be sure, but a teen nonetheless, and she liked to remind me of this fact at the most inauspicious times. It was a bit of a shock to my Dayton, Ohio–grown sensibilities to think that my face was in the cunt of a girl who was still in her Garanimals while I was fucking Tony Connors in the backseat of his grandmother's Olds 88. Still, I sport more Roman Polanski-esque tendencies than the average bulldyke, so the thought that I was fucking a girl within actual spitting distance of my Daddy/girl fantasies was, after the requisite flash of feminist guilt, actually quite the handy little fetish.

"I think it's an especially good way to talk to a teenager like you, Sugar. Now, grab onto my neck, keep your cunt spread, and straddle my face with that hot little teenage pussy of yours." She smiled down at me like it was her idea, and finally put her soft, sweet lips and swollen slit on my voracious mouth.

I took her in with my tongue all at once, my boots digging into the floor, and my hips thrusting hard against the wall as I rubbed her little girl cunt all over my face. I entered her and ripped her apart with my mouth, lifting her up higher to thrust my tongue into her hole, all the while pounding my hips into the wall like a dog humping air. She rocked her tight little ass into me and spread her fine, fresh come all over my face and into my sucking mouth. Her girlish whimpers blended with my deep, rough groans as I pushed deeper into her and furiously rubbed my own clit against the seam of my jeans. All at once, she moved her hands from my neck and tore into my hair as she exploded into my face with several jerky thrusts.

"Oh God, Daddy! Oh, oh, yes, Daddy, take me!"

Come poured all over my chin and down the front of me, and as I let her post-orgasmic body slide down my torso, she looked at me with a bit of real submission in her eyes, and then some embarrassment. I think she was more surprised than I was at her sincerity.

I decided to make the best of my advantage and treat her like a bitch for as long as I could; I knew I was on borrowed time.

"You wanna be Daddy's little bitch, don't you baby? I know you do, girl. Daddy's here for you, girl."

I grabbed her hips roughly, bent her over, and spread her right there in the hall on all fours. Her face was in the carpet, her legs were spread as far as she could stretch them, and she had brought her Mac-shel-lacked fingernails back to her cunt and was holding it open for me. I decided to take her ass first, barely touching her cunt. I coated my fingers with her come and moved her hands up to her ass, so she could open herself for me there. I held her tight little body by the crook of her hip, my palm covering about half of her ass. I started rocking her slowly, massaging her hole, and then eased her back gently onto my fingers.

She let out a high femme moan that made me want to plow her, but I settled on kicking her legs farther apart and plunging my hand deeper inside her ass. As fortuitous happenstance would have it, a small bottle of lube was at the ready there in the hall: I coated my hand generously and held her ass open while I poured some into her.

"Oh, Jesus, Daddy, my asshole is so tight! Take my hole, fuck it! Fuck me, Daddy!"

Now, these words would have put me over the top if they'd been uttered by a World Wide Federation wrestler, but hearing them from this stunningly gorgeous, high femme, hard-core top, bent over, with my hand inside her ass, incited me to excess. I pulled her head back by her hair, grabbed her hip, and pulled her hard toward me, and I thrust my hand into her, first, three, then four fingers. I pumped her furiously; she was all moans and cries, and I was sweating and fucking her intensely. Her body bucked up as she climaxed hard and tight around my hand.

And then, the most curious thing happened—bubbles started flowing out of her ass. Suddenly, I went from Monster Top to Bobby and Cindy Brady after a mishap with an overfilled washing machine. What I had thought was lube was actually the same company's brand of sex toy cleaner.

Only to me. Only I could have this flawless creature on all fours calling me "Daddy," coming and oblivious, while I watch bubbles foam from her anus. I recovered from the visual spectacle in time to start scooping the bubbles out of her ass. *Jesus, the nonoxynol 9.* I was trying to rock this chick's world, and instead I was going to end up numbing out her lower intestine.

"Give your little ass to Daddy, baby, I wanna make you feel real good," I said as I began furiously sucking toy cleaner out of her, spitting the vile stuff into my hand, and then going back for more, like some pornographic takeoff on a Laurel and Hardy bucket brigade.

"Oh, yeah, that feels good," she said as I sucked out the last putrid bit of the detergent. *That's it,* I thought.

"That's a very good girl," I mumbled. She turned around in my arms, and I smiled as I tried to conceal the numbing effect of the cleaner on my lips and tongue.

We had spent three hours at my apartment and had made no progress whatsoever in our scholastic inquires into the nature of gender among the Bolivians. I was ravenous.

"Are you hungry now, Honey?" I asked.

"I could be cajoled, I suppose."

"So I noticed," I said as I reached down, squeezed her left nipple, and kissed her.

We went to the corner restaurant for a bite to eat. After dinner, we walked through the neighborhood with my hand slipped in between two of the front buttons of her coat, and inside the slit of the lycra dress that had earlier proved itself so amenable to our activities. I led her down Castro Street with two of my fingers in her cunt, and took her one block farther to Collingwood Park, a place infamous for the sexual opportunities it affords the men of our famed district.

As we walked around the perimeter of the park, we were vaguely harassed as breeder voyeurs, which I attributed to both my high butch appearance and a lack of imagination on the part of the fags in attendance. She was a bit hesitant, but I moved us through their cruising territory and right into the dead-center of the park.

"What are you doing?" she asked.

I gave her my John Holmes stare again and pushed her up against a well-lit fence; the ground around it was covered with broken glass and reeked of male piss.

It was no *Wuthering Heights,* but it had its appeal.

"You aren't really going to—I mean, it's *their* park," she said, referring to the men waiting on the sidewalk like junior high school girls at their first mixer.

"We pay our taxes, don't we?" I asked as I kissed her and held her tight against the fence. I unbuttoned her coat and thrust my knee between her legs to spread her. I shielded her body from the light with my own, grabbed the fence near her head, and thrust my hand between her bare legs, rocking the steel behind her. I kicked her legs farther apart, and her expensive heels scraped along the pavement as I entered her, hard. I stuck my fingers down her throat so that she would have something to suck on while I pumped the come out of her still-wet cunt. I fucked her mercilessly there, in the middle of that park, four fingers pounding into her, my teeth clenched into her neck, and her fingernails digging straight through my jacket into the flesh of my biceps. She threw her head back against the fence and then transformed a silent scream into deep bruises on my arms as she came in tight contractions that strangled my fingers. I cupped my hand around her abraded cunt and held her like that for a while, there in Collingwood Park, before we walked back to my place.

Fucking another top is indeed a curious affair, which lends itself to both trepidation and paranoia. You see, no matter how amenable the other top may be to your ministrations at the moment, there is a little meter in her head that is constantly measuring the exact amount of domination and force to which you have subjected her, in order to repay you in kind at some later hour. Now this terrifies me, because, well, I just don't think many of my finest moments have been with my ass in the air. I feel like a turtle on its back, and I have enchanted former lovers who have tried to flip me with a fetching "For God's sake, let me do it!" attitude that has more frequently moved them to tears than me to orgasm.

She wasn't having it; once we were back at my apartment, the hour of reckoning had arrived.

"Down."

In the intervening moments (which now seemed like light years) since I'd had her against the fence, she had apparently regained the high femme top fierceness that rendered me a slave boy at her feet. She demanded worship, and her body and bearing made it difficult to refuse.

"Excuse me?" I attempted to reel the words back into my mouth as soon as they escaped.

"What about 'down' don't you understand?"

This time, I dropped awkwardly to my knees and looked up at her for further instruction.

"I think it's time for *you* to be naked." Like many butch tops, I cling to my clothes like a life raft during sex, and parting with them so unceremoniously was a trifle disconcerting.

"Take your shirt off, baby, let's see what you've got under there." I pulled off my black T-shirt quickly, like a band-aid, and revealed a serviceable white 42D Bali underwire, sans floral cleavage decoration, which I had at no time regarded as a sex toy.

"Very nice," she laughed, and suddenly I was ten and shirtless on the basketball court in Robby and Phillip Miller's backyard, where a scandalized Mrs. Miller returned home and brusquely corrected my impropriety.

"And in here?"

I restrained myself from assisting her in unfastening my industrial-strength brassiere, but eventually she managed to unhook the contraption, and she held my large breasts by the nipples for a moment before she freed them. She then had me stand up and take off my metal and leather belt, along with my pole climbers and black jeans. The latter had been concealing a huge boner I had packed in my jockstrap before we had left, which was now bulging conspicuously before her.

"A present, I see. How delightful." I felt like I was living in *Emmanuelle III in 3-D.*

"Lie down, face up, *now.*"

I complied and she took off her dress for effect, but kept those lethal, now damaged, stilettos on her tiny feet. She then rested the toe of her shoe on my cock and said, "You look so pretty lying underneath my feet. I could keep you here forever."

She traced the outline of my shaft with the heel of her shoe, and I trembled as if it had been attached to me by nerves and muscle instead of leather. As she walked up toward my head, she traced the contours of my body with her heel, and upon arriving there, she planted her left foot next to my face.

"Lick it, boy."

I delineated her entire shoe delicately with my tongue, as though the thin leather were her pussy lips, and I immersed myself in the curve of her instep. She kicked my head away cruelly and thrust the heel into my mouth, and I sucked it rhythmically in response to her delicate thrusts. She then walked back to the middle of my body, slipped her foot between the divide of my legs, and pressed into my flesh with that heel of hers, stabbing at my cock before she made a slow and painful journey up to my chest. Once there, she extracted the retribution she evidently felt was due her, and dug the heel of her shoe into my sternum.

Jesus. The shoe-licking's one thing, but Good Lord, really, this is a bit much.

She looked down at me and laughed as though she were keeping score—and winning.

I was shaking, as much from arousal as from pain and equivocation. She knelt down beside me, kissed the heel marks she had left on my body, and kissed my face in an almost maternal way.

"Now isn't this better, baby?" She said as she pinched my nipples and kissed me again before slapping me hard in the face.

Mother-fucking bitch. I stifled my tears; I wasn't going to let her have that part of me. She saw the frailty I tried to hide from her and laughed as she straddled my face with her perfect cunt and allowed me to suck come from her. She ran me back and forth over the edge between trust and suspicion, and I trusted her just enough to make her dangerous to me.

She pulled away from me and let the cold air hit my come-wet face.

"There, baby. Get on your hands and knees, and keep your head down."

I wanted to trust her enough to let go, yet I was still wavering. I heard her rustling through my things, and when she returned, the first thing I felt was my own heavy leather belt doubled over, metal side out, caressing my inner thighs and the cheeks of my ass. She started whipping me, hard, with little ceremony, and it became increasingly difficult to stifle my tears as she persisted.

Jesus. Damn her, she could care less about how I feel. That's it. Just as I was about to pull myself up from the realm of bottoming and stop her, she dropped the belt.

"Had enough?" She asked, and I raised my red face up, trying hard to hold back the tears.

I've had enough all right, you she-devil.

"Poor baby," she cooed, only half-sarcastically. She directed me to lie on the bed face up, and I hesitated a moment before I obeyed the command I had just been ready to undermine. I could sense some contrition in her bearing, and we did have this tacit switching agreement. And then there was my remorse over the bubbles. I have a capacity for guilt that a team of Jewish mothers, working night and day through my formative years, would be proud of. I once again acquiesced to her will.

She straddled my legs and began to massage the large bulge in my jockstrap. I felt at once enraged, rebellious, coddled, hard, and hurt. She talked to me in a mother's voice and told me that she was going to make me feel very good; then she rubbed her big, soft tits over my cock and between my thighs. She asked me how old I was, and I looked up at her with a tattered, fledgling machismo, shaved twelve years off of my age, and replied, "I'm seventeen."

She must have truly felt bad for whipping me so hard, because she then did something she'd promised me she'd never do—she started to give me a blow job. She eased herself farther down the bed, so that her face was directly over my quivering cock. She then nuzzled the soft cotton of my bleached-white Calvin Klein jockstrap and asked me if any of my girlfriends had ever sucked my cock before, to which I replied, "Well, last summer, this girl who was a counselor at the day camp I was workin' at started blowin' me in the equipment shack, but some idiot kid came in right when she was about to start sucking on my rod, and then she was too freaked to ever try it again." I do a mean seventeen-year-old boy.

"Well, you're going to become a man tonight, baby, 'cause Momma's going to give you a blow job you'll never forget."

She peeled my jockstrap back gingerly with her teeth, and from the white cotton emerged the eight-inch Super Realistic I had packed in her honor; it felt all the more realistic with her sweet snatch poised above it. She pulled her body back and nestled her gorgeous face against my swollen cock head, and then she slowly drew her tongue up the shaft and around, carefully covering every millimeter of this huge cock that had become my own. She went down lower and sucked on each of my balls, and as she did, the rest of the dick balanced against her cheek, bouncing against her face like in the porno movie scenes I replay in my head when I jack off. She drew the tip of her tongue up along the bottom of my cock until she was at the head, on which she placed a sweet little kiss that made me want to face-fuck her; naturally, I refrained. She slid her lips around the head of my cock so excruciatingly slowly that I had to restrain my hips from thrusting into her.

"What a big, hard dick you have, baby; you're bigger than most grown men. I bet you'd like to stick that big dick in Mommy's mouth, now wouldn't you?"

Well, I would indeed. I wondered briefly whether silence or a response would make her continue, and opted for the former.

"You want me to take your seventeen-year-old cock down my throat? Is that right? Well, okay, baby, I guess there are many forms of torture."

With that, she took the entire head in her mouth, drew the air from within her cheeks, and swirled her tongue around it while she began to suck. I wanted to slam my whole shaft down her throat, hard, but she corrected my instincts with a glare that told me to stay back on the bed and be seventeen. I fought every impulse I had developed in my illustrious career as a butch top and tried to remember the stress reduction techniques I had learned in my math anxiety seminar thirteen years before. Breathing exercises may have improved my SAT score, but nothing could have prepared me for her deep-throat artistry: she grazed the top of my cock head with her teeth before suddenly swallowing all eight inches down her throat. She closed her eyes when she had me there, all the way to the balls in her beautiful face, moaning as if my cock were rubbing up against her G-spot every time she wrung it with her lips. Holding back was excruciating, and I was jittery and nearly hollow with desire. She looked up at me, measured my need, and smiled as if she owned me. She then went back to her sucking, moaning, and smiling, all the while holding me down with the slightest pressure from her index fingers.

I wanted to rape her.

She allowed my cock to slide slowly out of her mouth, and she smiled down at me as she mounted me as if I were her steed. She pushed my legs together so that the shaft stood straight up, parted her lips, and lightly grazed the head of my cock back and forth with the wetness of her pussy as she straddled it. She then moved up to my face and spread her lips, so that I could see the inside of the snatch I wasn't fucking. It was pink and smooth on the outside, and a deeper teenage rose color on the inside, which was coated with a slick, milky whiteness. Farther inside, I could see she was contracting her walls for my benefit—alternating a slow, thick, cock-sucking motion with more rapid, squeezing movements.

"You want to fuck this, don't you? You want to ram your hard cock inside my pussy right now, you son of a bitch."

She really did have a certain flair for torture. She held herself just close enough to me so that I could smell her cunt and feel its heat, but she drew it out of reach whenever I lifted up to make contact. By the time she withdrew herself completely, my neck was sore, my hips were thrusting, and I had a hard-on that could have fucked through steel. She laughed at my predicament as if I had indeed been her animal; as if she were taunting my hard horse-dick with her crop for her own amusement.

She lifted herself back so that her cunt was once more arched above my tortured cock. By this point, if there had been blood running through my balls, it would have been ice blue. She took my cock in one hand and smiled again at me, in my pathetic state. She never broke, but she finally parted those velvet lips of hers and held herself above me so that my cock was held lightly in her pussy. She slowly swallowed my whole head inside her, and though I quivered with the intensity of the scene, I was reluctant even then to give myself over to my desire. Then, in the same way she'd taken the whole of my cock down her throat, she slid down my huge shaft until it amazingly disappeared completely inside her petite body. She closed her eyes and moaned deeply, and I put my hands on her smooth hips, started thrusting, and finally eased into the act like I had the million times I'd done it before.

Or so I thought.

"Just what the *fuck* do you think you're doing? Stay still and keep your hands where I put them." She stuck my hands under my ass and I lay there like a mummy, my body tight, an immovable, bound package, ready to come undone as she rode my cock. I was on the verge of leaving my body when a brutal slap stunned me across my face and woke me from my stupor.

"This is the way it will always be with us; this is the way it should be."

Time moved in slow motion for a moment as I allowed the rage to register in my brain. *How fucking* dare *she. That's enough. That is most certainly enough.* I felt the blood swell in my face and my heart throbbing in my ears, and I threw her off of me and yelled, "That's it! *That is it.* I've had it. You like it rough, baby? Well, you can have it rough, right here, right now, bitch."

I flipped her over on her hands and knees, thrust my cock deep into her tight cunt, pulled her back by her hair, and told her, "I'll be as vicious as you are long before you're as strong as me." I started fucking her as if I had just been released from prison.

She reached back and spread her cunt open for me as I shoved her face down into the bed. I grabbed her hips as if they were handles and plowed her like a jackhammer. She had built a massive load up in me, and her cruelty and domination moved my topping pendulum so off the charts that I fucked her brutally. I kicked her legs apart, mounted her, and held her body down with my weight, while I pinched both of the nipples on her big tits with one hand. I gathered both of her thin wrists in the other while I tore into her tight slit with my steel cock. I ravaged her cunt continually and yelled, "You'll always top me? You will not always top me, bitch!"

All at once, her cunt became thick around my dick, I released my hold on her wrists, and she reached forward, grabbed a pillow, and screamed; her body heaved up in jerky movements underneath me.

But I was far from done with her. The tension wrought up in me from bottoming to her made me a maniacal top. I turned her over while I was still inside her, put her ankles on my shoulders, and regained the momentum of moments before. Then I reached down and grabbed the steel of the bed frame and fucked her across the mattress for hours until her head bobbed off the edge, again invoking the skin flicks to which I jack off.

Though my rage began to subside, the animalism remained; I grunted with every hard thrust into her. She received me with her entire body; her hips tilted upward, her legs wrapped around my back, and she sucked my dick tight inside her cunt until we were both dripping with sweat and our bodies were sliding across each other. Finally, my clit swelled until it filled the container of the cock inside her. She took a deep breath in and threw her head back, and I felt her pussy start to vibrate with orgasm around me. When she tore down my hypersensitive back with her long fingernails, I bolted into her with a brutal, cathartic intensity. I fell into the largesse of her breasts, and I swear to God, I saw a white light there that mirrored the explosions in my cunt.

I took my dick off, soothed my soaking wet, leather-worn cunt with my fingers, and climbed into bed naked next to her. She drew my head into her breasts for an eternity; my jaw slackened, and I released what felt like twenty-nine years of controlled pressure into her tits. I unleashed a powerful sigh into that deep cleavage and followed the white light I found there as if I were being led across the divide. Her tits were round and soft, teenager and Mommy at the same time. The power of them relegated me once more to a shy, youthful submission, but this time, when she asked me how old I was, I looked up at her bashfully and said, "I'm eight."

"What a good, sweet boy you are. I bet you want to suck Momma's pussy." She spread her legs, parted her lips, and pushed my head down to her cunt. I sucked her cunt as if it were all I needed to survive. I yielded to her in earnest, there, between her legs, at her feet, under her control. I offered up my will in protracted gasps, and at once, a tight, archaic mass in me unclenched, and I was made free.

The Punishment Fits the Crime

Paula K. Clearwater

I was a graduate student, a schoolteacher's daughter, a law-abiding citizen of moderate income. What happened to me was one of the most embarrassing events of my life. And I masturbate to the memory of it.

My first class that day wasn't until the late afternoon. I left the house early, feeling a gnawing yearning for something I couldn't identify. I was bored with that overwhelming nagging anxiety that school had always provoked in me—a sense that my time was never wholly my own, that I had to steal it from the avalanche of work that was always waiting to be done.

I was anxious for freedom and for something fresh that smacked of luxury and abandon. Just about anything would do. Sex would be nice. But pure, unadulterated sex for its own sake, without all the contraptions of relationship...Men know how to release through sex. They use each other. It's contractual, understood. But this is not something women do. So, what could I do in just a few short hours that would satisfy my craving? I drove on the highway in the direction of campus, teasing myself with the thought of veering west on some road heading away from Boston. I approached an exit I used to take with a friend when we were hungry for a shopping adventure. The exit led to a strip lined with discount brand-name stores, providing us a whole day's uninterrupted entertainment. We'd find a designer double-breasted wool vest that had been marked down to a steal because it had gotten separated from the matching skirt. Other gorgeous clothes, which had been lost under the surface for months because they had been mismarked for size, would resurface on the littered shores of an end-of-the-season clearance sale, and we'd net them in. We'd shop until we were exhausted, revel in our purchases over a dinner out, and then go to my apartment, where we'd pull all our new clothes out of the bags and orgiastically brandish them, gloating over our ability to spot a good deal. A significant part of the fun was in finding the best values for the least money.

I turned off the exit ramp and headed for the biggest store. If I couldn't get sex, a shopping spree—a good dose of self-indulgence—would do the trick. I grabbed a cart inside the door and wheeled to the clearance section. My disappointment was audible when I discovered that a huge sale was just ending, and the remaining stuff was pretty picked over. I'd seen the day when I would never have let a sale like that go by. An aching emptiness floated up from my belly like a giant glass ball wedging itself under my rib cage. I desperately fooled myself into thinking I liked a certain silk blouse. I tossed it into the cart and plodded along, feeling less and less inspired by the minute. Nothing worthwhile. Convinced that I had mined the clearance rack, I threw the silk blouse back and strolled off.

But with a renewed spark, I started toward the center aisles, where racks had been freshly packed with the season's hot new items. Among them, I found a short, flippy, fully lined spring skirt and a soft, creamy blouse that complemented it perfectly. The skirt was the rusty pink color of late hydrangea blossoms just before they turn. It had tiny ebony buttons along the side that made it look a little old-fashioned, even for its skimpy length. The blouse, antique white with a tailored three-quarter sleeve, had a plunging neckline collared with a fine detail of subtle lace. Together, they'd create the image of a slightly naughty 1930s schoolgirl. Fueled by the adrenaline high of a good find, I tossed them into the basket, feeling my spirits waft into light, and went in search of shoes to match.

The shoes were displayed at the back of the store. On my way to them, I passed the lingerie. A huge bin had been loaded with panties, and another held bras. I was delighted when I found a matching satiny pale green set with ecru lace that looked like decorative icing. And then I found a garter belt that also matched. I didn't usually bother with them since pantyhose were so much easier, but the trio was splendid. I whirled around to the other side of the aisle and found a perfect eggshell-color pair of hose. The frosting on the cake was a pair of black high heels that I absolutely adored. They were a little higher than I was used to, but they had the best way of showing off my long legs and of making me stand tall and brazen. I had to have them.

In the heat of the moment, I remembered to look at my watch. "Shit!" I was going to be late for class—a rather important one, at that. I threw the shoes into the cart and turned toward the register. "Geez," I thought. "I haven't even looked at the prices of this stuff!" I reached in and pulled it all out. My heart sank as I realized that the prices of in-season merchandise added up to a lot more than I was used to spending on a student's budget. But I just *had* to have it all. My chest caved thinking of the fun

I'd have in the skirt. And there's something so indulgent about knowing that you're wearing beautiful lingerie, even if no one ever sees it. If only it weren't quite so expensive.

In an instant, before I could think twice about it, I scooped up the lingerie and shoved it into my purse. I'm sure I immediately flushed with terror. I glanced around like a timid squirrel, trying to determine if anyone had been around. My ears pounded. My palms greased the handle of the cart. I tottered along, trying to appear casual. My instincts told me to try to pretend, even to myself, that I had done nothing. My throat felt like it was being shoved open with a cardboard tube. I couldn't swallow. Instead, I just kept walking, eyes bugged out, hands gripping and sliding, knees wobbling as though I were navigating over a cobblestone alley. The path up to the register seemed infernally long.

Only when I stood in line did I realize that I was going to have to pull out my wallet. How was I going to do that without the lingerie falling out of my purse? I started to panic. I was already on borrowed time. I couldn't possibly go all the way to the back of the store, or to the dressing room, or anywhere else. Surely, before I reached the front of the line, I would have a chance to get my wallet out.

I found myself facing awkwardly away from the register, trying not to open my purse any more than I had to. I started to fish for my wallet when, to my horror, I saw that one of the garter straps was trailing outside of the purse like a tentacle, looking as though it were trying to escape. It was wrapped around a little pink triangle I had pinned to the outside pocket. I lost the last shred of cool I had. Slamming the pocketbook back under my arm, I simultaneously tried to stuff the dangling strap inside.

A woman without a shopping cart had come up behind me as the line moved up. She eyed me quizzically as I maniacally wrestled with my purse. My underarms were drenched with sweat, which smelled strange: a sharp, malodorous sour brine. My throat twisted into a taut rope, cutting off my air. I thought I'd faint. As the line shifted to move up once more, I saw that I'd have to act fast. I went to the front of my cart, and using the woman ahead of me as a block, fished into my purse and extracted my wallet. I then quickly placed my things on the counter, trying to act as naturally as anyone can who is about to pass out with terror. As I offered the cashier my credit card, my hands shook so noticeably that she asked me if I was all right.

"I need food," I said, thinking quickly.

She made small talk, saying that she gets like that, too. The pedestrian smile on the woman's face and the tiny blessed slice of normal conversation soothed my nerves. My purchases bagged, I bounded for the door, taking off without my copy of the signed receipt. The cashier scurried through the door after me with it, tagging me on the back and blasting my cannonball stomach through my heart.

I couldn't feel my legs. But somehow, they were taking me to the car. If only they could take flight! "Get out your keys," I said aloud to myself.

"Miss?" I heard the voice but kept on walking. The voice repeated. My chest pounded.

"Miss?" I clutched my purse tighter and ignored the voice, denying it was real until it was right behind me. "Excuse me, Miss?!"

The woman was tall and broad. She was wearing jeans and a man's white shirt. Staggeringly butch. She pulled an identification card from her back pants pocket, and introducing herself as a store detective, slowed to a stop a slight distance from me. I was aware of the distance, as though she were a bit farther away than a stranger would normally stand.

"Ma'am, I believe you have something belonging to the store. Would you come back in with me so that we can discuss it?"

I thought to argue, but my voice wouldn't engage. As I walked with her across the parking lot, I wished that I could take back my actions...everything that had led up to this moment. I kept moving further and further back into the day, first wishing I hadn't stolen the lingerie, then wishing I hadn't even seen it. I wished I hadn't come to the store, or gotten off the exit, or left the house early.

I fought the urge to cry as she took me to an office above the front of the store. She could have been leading me to a secret dungeon—I'd never been aware that an office or anything else existed up there. A wall of dark glass lined the balcony overlooking the store. What looked to shoppers like a glitzy reflective facade was a line of windowed offices. As I looked out over the floor, I gasped at how easy it was to see the whole shoe department...how easy it was, in fact, to see every part of the entire store. In addition, the office was equipped with a couple of televisions that were flashing close-ups of the registers, the area outside the fitting rooms, the leather goods area, and gift ware. My head wanted to explode. What was going to happen next? Were the police on their way already? Would I be locked up? Fined? Featured on the nightly news? For a second I felt so out of my body that I wasn't sure whether I had wet myself. I looked at the detective, hoping for the slightest sprig of humanity.

She was very self-assured and composed. She had me empty out my purse. My shame sapped me as I took out my wallet, comb, keys, date book, some make-up, an open bag of M&M peanuts, and some mail. She took an inventory of it all, counting my money, copying information from my license, and filling out several forms she had torn from a pad. She had me sign the forms, then motioned for me to sit down. She took the lingerie with her and left the office, saying that I could put the rest of the stuff back in my purse. I sat, gazing over the store, which now seemed quite foreign to me. I watched with envy as "normal" citizens shopped at leisure, enjoying their freedom while I was missing my class. But what was going to happen to me? Flashes of shame and fear careened through me like home videos shifting discordantly from one image to the next. How could I face my friends or family if they knew? What if my boss found out?

When she returned, the detective had the stolen articles in a plastic bag stapled with the forms. "Exhibit A," I thought. She swung her chair around to face me. I cringed, averting my eyes. For what seemed like a long time, she scrutinized me while I glanced between her shoulder and the floor. Finally she spoke. "Well, you know," she said. "I guess you realize that you're in a whole heap of trouble."

I nodded, looking her in the eyes for the first time. They were absorbing and spirited at once, bouncing me like a ball on a string.

"I've got pictures of you. And they're very incriminating." She swirled around in her chair, pressed a few buttons, and pointed toward the television screens. One showed a still shot of me stashing the merchandise in my purse. On the other was a close-up of the strap hanging from my bag. It was amazingly sharp and focused. I shuddered.

She leaned toward me, resting her elbows on her knees and craning close to my face.

"There are more, too. We have everything we need to make a case out of this." I closed my eyes, not breathing.

"But you and I have a little something in common." She leaned back without turning away from me, and hit a button again. On the screen flashed another close-up of my pink triangle.

"We're family," she smiled, leaning way back in the chair. "So, I'm going to try to help you out a little. But I'm not letting you off the hook. No, Honey," she laughed. "I work too hard at my job, and pride myself too much to let you get away without *some* kind of payback. We have to come to an understanding." She stretched like a dog prompting play, stood up, and leaned her considerable bulk against the desk, folding her arms in front of her.

I was so tremendously relieved that I almost leapt up to hug her. I told her that I was willing to do anything to avoid prosecution. I appreciated the chance to repay the store. I'd be happy to pay for the stuff right now...whatever. I jabbered on, trying to belie the fact that I knew she was up to something I couldn't possibly be prepared for. But the detective looked askance at me, amused. She stepped up and took my face in her hand. Her smile was warm and disarmingly engaging.

"Sweetheart, what I'm willing to do for you is to let you keep this our personal little secret. Only you and I need know about it. But, in order for me to share the weight of your guilt, you're going to have to let me assuage mine in some way. I find myself in a rather compromising position, too. I could lose my job over something like this."

I felt her heat and swallowed hard. She was right up close to me. Her eyes penetrated me. I seeped out from under her gaze and surveyed the whole scene in my mind's eye, as if I were suddenly perched on the ceiling. She hovered while I cowered, thinking it over, my insides twisting into sinew, tight and waxy. I nodded my consent.

"Okay," she started. "This is how it's going to be. I'm not going to deal with this right now, because my colleague will be back here in a few minutes. I will be holding the merchandise, the tapes, and your signed statement here. I'm not going to show them to anyone unless you don't keep your end of the bargain." I nodded again. "Here's the deal. You come back here tonight after the store closes at 10:30, and wait in the side lot for me to let you in that side door." She pointed toward it. "I have to work late, so we'll be alone then. You should be prepared to accept your punishment at that time. You don't show up, I send all this stuff to the police."

I agreed, and I was shown unceremoniously through another door in the front.

The rest of the day I did little more than play the whole event over and over in my mind. I would relive the excruciating embarrassment and terror each time as if it were happening anew. I sat on my couch, gazing out the window, hearing the phone ring as if it were someone else's in the distance, unaware that the room had darkened until I could barely see. Somewhere in the din I remembered that I had left my package in the office. Perhaps she had kept it for "collateral." It was still hours before I could go and get this thing over with. What was she going to do? I had heard stories about dykes who were into dominance/submission. How far did they go? I tried to remember everything I had ever heard. If only I could talk to someone about it. I thought about the way the detective moved. She was strong, cocky. Why shouldn't she have been? She had me by the short hairs, and I collapsed thinking about it, feeling like a wayward child. Or, was I swooning? What would it be like to be captive to her unyielding certainty?

I ached, and reeked of the acrid scent of fear. I ran a bath and sank below the steamy water, trying to drown the incessant ranting in my head.

When the time came, I parked in the side lot. The detective ushered me in. Once again, she led me up the stairs. The store was even more eerie than before, without lights or people. My heart drummed as she quietly closed the door behind us. I stood in the middle of the room. She threw some keys onto the desk, turned against it, and observed me.

"Take off your coat," she said. I laid it on the chair. She shifted and lowered her voice. "Now take off your clothes."

My body turned toward the door involuntarily. She asked me if I'd changed my mind. But, of course, I hadn't. I faced her and started to undress. When I had stripped down to my underclothes, she tossed the bag of my new clothes at my feet. The lingerie was in it.

"Put it all on," she commanded. And I did.

She made me squirm under her impassive surveillance as I stripped naked and slipped on the new things. The lingerie was gorgeous. It fit perfectly. I fastened the garter belt and then decided to put on the skirt before the stockings. But she made me put the stockings on first. I fumbled with the package. She rescued me, cutting the tough plastic with scissors. I smoothed the stockings on and dressed in the skirt and blouse. She cut the string that bound the two shoes, and I slid into them. Brushing back my long hair, I stood before her, feeling a strange combination of poise, dread, and a titillating, burning shyness.

Now that I had the whole outfit on, it felt nothing like the sort of thing I usually wear. It was as if some subterfuged personality had taken me shopping that day. Though my good Catholic upbringing had squelched lots of my baser impulses, they would not be conquered—the red stain of the "femme slut" would ooze out of me. It was as if the *clothes* had shopped for *me,* and they had better ideas about what I was doing in them than I did.

And here I was, under the approving eye of this outrageous bull dyke. Totally at her behest, I felt sexy and alive for the first time in a long time. I waited while she inspected me. She commanded me to walk over to a mirror that hung behind the door.

"Why don't you check out your pretty little outfit for yourself?" she suggested.

While I uncomfortably contemplated my adorned image, she talked to me about what a terrible, unlawful thing I'd done stealing from the company, taking stuff that wasn't mine. I listened to every word, mortified by her reprimanding tone. I hated looking at myself while she talked; I felt abashed, anxious to be punished and absolved. I wanted it over with.

She walked to the door, opened it, and invited me out ahead of her, leading me down the metal stairs again, out into the store. My heels clanked and echoed with each step. The bright lights from the parking lot illuminated the massive space, robbing the color from the racks of clothes, bathing them in sharp, garish blue-gray shadows the color of old third-rate black-and-white movies.

Seeming to sense my hesitance, she put her arm around my shoulder and guided me to the back of the store, over to the lingerie section. There, she made me bend over the bin of panties, sinking my face into their soft silkiness. For a moment I had second thoughts.

"Turn your head this way," she said, directing me to face a full-length mirror at the foot of the aisle. "That way, you can watch while I spank you," she jeered.

I bristled, but I felt my clit clinch. It was so humiliating. I wanted it to start. She lifted my skirt above my hips and began to spank me with her bare hand. She stood to the side so as not to block my view. I saw her check out the reflected panoptic, as well.

She spanked me for what seemed like half an hour, increasing the severity of the slapping all the while. It was such a relief to surrender to the apex of all that had brought me to that moment. Finally, the tension was streaming out of me. My fear melted into my flesh, which, in turn, gave way to her solid resolve. My bottom writhed with heat, and I was getting turned on. I couldn't help it. I wanted to scream, but I was afraid. She began chiding me and making humiliating references to my position—accurately describing the punishment's contradictory effects on me. I squirmed and whimpered as the pain intensified, but she kept on in an increasing rhythm. I started to cry. My bottom bucked against her iron hand, and I tried to wriggle away, to no avail. I caught a view of my gleaming satin rump undulating to her tempo as she leaned her other hand into the small of my arched back, pinning me deeper into the cushion of panties. I started to scream, releasing a torrent of tears into the folds of silky fabric. A strand of lace scratched my cheek.

"Go ahead and scream," she chided. "No one can hear you. You might as well."

I cried harder, kicking and bucking for all I was worth. My bottom burned. My clit hardened, reddened, and gushed. She knew it, too. She was moving in rhythm with me, rocking, pressing against me, tempering my fight. My clit tightened and I felt as if I'd explode. At her final thrust, I screamed, flailing wildly, coming in waves and sending underwear gushing over the sides of the bin. She cried out, as well. But I had stopped looking into the mirror; I was burying my face into the mound of panties, wetting them with my tears, and dissolving into their delicate folds.

I rolled over and lay in the sea of lingerie for a few minutes while she moved something into place. Then she helped me up and straightened me out, the way a parent would fix a disheveled child. She leaned me against the mirrored column and held me for a few minutes. Then we went silently back upstairs. While I put on my coat, she filled my bag with the clothes I'd worn there. She threw the signed forms in with them.

"You'll have to trust me. I've already erased the film," she said quietly. "The truth is, if you hadn't come back, there wouldn't have been much I could've done about it, having already let you go. But I knew you'd come."

I choked back a laugh at her double entendre. She spoke even more softly now, pulling my coat collar right-side out and flattening it with her hand. "Are you okay?"

I answered, "I'm still wearing the stolen goods."

"That's okay," she replied. "There's no return on worn underwear."

She walked me to the door. On the drive home, I felt clean—cleaner than I'd ever felt before, lighter and more alive.

In the weeks and months that followed, I asked myself about what I had done. Why had I shoplifted the lingerie in the first place? Had I wanted to be caught? Was the whole event inspired by the driving need of my dying spirit? Was it greed, or stupidity, frustration, or divine intervention? Did I, just for once, want to have the experience of having something without having to pay for it? Over the months, I discovered something about myself. For one thing, I had been taking life a little too seriously. And for another, nice Catholic girls like me don't don nor do they shed their panoply of guilt as easily as slipping a new dress on or off. I learned that trying on something new is much easier and more satisfying when guided by an appreciative hand and when sallied by a force from without. I learned it over and over again.

Just Drops

Ruth Gifford

A birthday present for atara from her Mistress.

"Of water?" Erin asked her lover, as she ran a hand through her short blond hair. "I don't get it. Is it going to be really cold water?"

Laurel smiled reassuringly. "Just water, and no, it won't be cold. Just a drop at a time."

Just a drop at a time? That doesn't sound so bad. Not like the cane or being flogged. Erin smiled to herself. *I can take that.* But she couldn't help being nervous, because Laurel had that smile on her face. And of course Laurel was going to tie her down for this; if Laurel thought she had to be tied down...well, it didn't bode well. Then again, maybe Laurel just wanted to see her tied down; she often did.

"Okay," she said aloud. "It sounds like fun."

Laurel chuckled. "I'm sure it will be."

She smiled and looked Erin over. As always, Erin felt small, somehow reduced by the fact that she had no clothing on while Laurel was fully dressed. Laurel didn't go in for formality; she liked Erin to call her Laurel even in the middle of a scene. But she did do some things traditionally; Erin was wearing a green leather collar that Laurel had locked on her a few minutes before. She always wore a silver ID bracelet with Laurel's name engraved on it; she'd worn it for three years now and never regretted it. Well, hardly ever. There were times when she was up on the St. Andrew's cross being flogged, before the endorphins had kicked in, when she would find herself wondering what she was doing there, letting this nice-looking, kindly eyed, soft-voiced bitch do these things to her. Those thoughts rarely lasted long, however. There was never any doubt in Erin's mind about who was in charge.

"Now, sweetheart, bring the labia spreader downstairs with you."

Erin grinned; she liked the labia spreader—it gave her a wonderful feeling of exposure. Sure, it was humiliating, but she liked being humiliated. And hurt, and teased, and...Her grin got broader as she rummaged through the lingerie drawer and pulled out a tangle of green leather. As she left the bedroom and headed for the stairs to the basement, she ran the leather straps through her fingers. Laurel just had to be different. It was a good thing that she also had the money to indulge herself. She liked seeing Erin in dark green leather, and so it was that simple: all of Erin's leather was dark green. Even in the Bay Area, that took some doing, and Erin knew that there were a couple of leather workers who had reason to be thankful for Laurel's particular tastes.

She tapped lightly on the basement door; this was one formality that Laurel insisted on.

"Come in, dear," Laurel called out, and Erin tried to look graceful as she walked into the room. "Now, let's get you into that."

A few minutes later, Erin was lying on the big table, which was covered with a rubber sheet. It felt clammy, and Erin was once again grateful that Laurel didn't go in for rubberwear. She'd seen people at parties dressed all in rubber and had always felt sorry for them. She looked to one side as Laurel moved into view.

"Where did you get that?" she asked, nodding her head toward the odd-looking stand that stood next to the table. Hanging on the stand was an enema bag.

"Greg had it. I think he adapted a plant shelf or something." Laurel's voice was matter-of-fact as she began to strap Erin onto the table. Erin tried to relax as her wrists were strapped down. Then Laurel moved to buckle a pair of thigh restraints onto her, and Erin began to worry a little.

"I'll have to give him a hard time," Erin said, trying to relax as Laurel fussed with her positioning. "Only dykes can do that kind of thing. Next thing you know, he'll be driving a truck."

"Now there's a scary thought. Okay, how are your legs doing?"

"Fine."

"Can they stay like that for a long time?"

"Sure." Erin gasped as Laurel ran a finger up the inside of one of her thighs. Then the waist restraint was being buckled down.

"Try to move." Erin squirmed. "Harder than that, really fight it." Once Erin had stilled, Laurel made some more adjustments. "Do it again. Okay, that's good." She swung the arm of the odd rack over the table.

"This reminds me of that episode of *Star Trek*. The one with the aliens doing experiments."

"That only describes thirty or so episodes. Now, listen to me." Laurel adjusted a hose that ran from the bag until the odd-looking tip at the end of the hose was positioned above Erin's cunt.

"Yes, Laurel."

"Like I told you, I'm going to let drops of water fall on you. One drop at a time, in a steady, regulated drip. You don' t have to do anything; just lie there and feel it."

"Yes, Laurel."

"Good girl." Laurel unclamped the hose, and Erin jumped as the first drop of water fell on her. "Did that hit your clit?"

"Not quite. It was a little above it."

Laurel fussed with things. "How about that?"

"Right on it."

"Good. Now be still, and be quiet. Or at least no talking."

"Yes. Laurel."

Laurel smiled, leaned down, and kissed Erin. She picked up the blindfold that had been resting on the table near Erin's head and fastened it on; then Erin heard her move off. Accustomed to listening for clues while she was blindfolded, Erin heard what she thought was Laurel sitting down. Yes, and she was reading; Erin could hear the pages turn.

That's it? Just drops of water falling on my clit? What's the big deal here? Why am I strapped down like she's going to be putting those horrible tiny clamps on me? Erin began to relax. The drops fell, one after the other, and it was actually rather pleasant to lie there and feel them. As Laurel had promised, the water wasn't all that cold, and the heat in the basement was turned up enough to keep Erin comfortable. Erin would have liked a little more attention, but she decided that Laurel undoubtedly knew what she was doing. *I wonder how often those are falling on me?* She tried to count them, but they were beginning to be too distracting. Drip, drip, drip. She was starting to anticipate each drop as it landed like the tap of a gentle finger against her clit; except no finger could be this steady. She was wanting to squirm now, but she couldn't because of the restraints.

Drip, drip, drip. She could feel her clit swelling, and she wondered how long she'd been here. She was getting more and more aroused. *I really like this; it's kind of soothing...almost meditative...*It would have been nice if Laurel had put some music on; it would have been something more to concentrate on as the drops fell.

Drip, drip, drip. *When will the next one...oh yeah...right there!* Erin really wished that the drops would fall harder, or maybe a little faster. Drip, drip, drip. She tried to angle herself to get more out of the drops, but of course she couldn't; she was strapped down too tight. She no longer heard the occasional sound of Laurel turning a page or the faint whir of the heater; all she could hear were the drips. Suddenly she realized that her mind was providing the noise. In reality, the drops made no sound at all. Erin began to get a little nervous; this was fucking with her head, and mind-games always scared her. As she began to feel fear, she could feel her cunt contract, and it seemed that her clitoris got even more swollen.

Drip, drip, drip. *I want to come...and I can't...oh this is awful...*Erin began to whimper. The drops felt like...what did they feel like? They burned her, as if the water were suddenly boiling or icy. She knew that this was just because she was so aroused that her clit was starting to register the sensation as pain. She felt almost as if that hard swollen knot of flesh were rising toward the water and then shrinking away when it landed. She no longer noticed the slickness of the wet rubber beneath her ass, or the feeling of the straps against her wrists and ankles. But she could still feel the straps against her thighs, and she suddenly realized that she felt them because she was straining against them with all her might. She tried to relax, but when she did, another drop landed, and she tensed up again. That set a pattern for a while; a drop would land, and she'd tense, and then she'd relax in the interval between it and the next one. There would always be a next one. *How long can this go on? I can't take much more of this.* She also realized that the odd little noises she was making, almost like choked-off whimpers, were coming out of her mouth in time to the drips.

Drip, drip, drip. *No...stop, say "stop"...but I said it was no big deal...oh God...*It hurt, but it wasn't like any other pain she'd felt. She tried to distract herself, thinking of scenes past. *Remember the first time she took me to a party?* It had been at the house of a friend of Laurel's, and Erin had wanted to back out of it. Laurel had looked at her and waited for Erin to say "stop" (the only safeword she had). Erin hadn't been able to, and the result had been that she'd ended up tied to a coffee table with her ass in the air while Laurel brought a paddle down on it. Her face had felt hotter than her ass when one of Laurel's friends had complimented Laurel on how good Erin looked in that position.

Drip, drip, drip. More memories...The buzz of the needle and the short sharp shocks (they had had a rhythm of their own, much like this water that was falling on her clit) as the tattoo artist had tattooed Laurel's symbol (a hand with a spiral on its palm) onto Erin's right hip. There had been an audience for that one as well. They'd been at a leather convention, and after the tattooing, Laurel had bent Erin over a horse and had caned her once for every year she'd been a free person. The cane landing on her skin had hurt, but not like this water that kept falling on her.

Drip, drip, drip. Erin opened her mouth to plead for it to stop, but remembered just in time that Laurel had said not to talk. Anyway, she wasn't ready to safeword, she just wanted to complain a little. Wait...she was actually getting close...Laurel hadn't said anything about not coming. Now if the drops would just come a little faster. No, they kept to their rhythm and she sobbed in frustration. *What about the time she used a needle on me?* But all Erin could remember about that scene was that Laurel had been very deliberate and methodical as she made scratches on Erin's skin.

Drip, drip, drip. Erin tried to contract her cunt in time to the drops, thinking that maybe she could get off that way. She had come once without being touched, as Laurel talked to her on the phone while Erin was at work. Laurel had told Erin to close her office door and sit at her desk with her legs spread as wide as her chair allowed.

"Now listen to my voice, start contracting your cunt, and keep your hands on the phone or on top of your desk." Laurel had then almost chanted (in a singsong rhythm like the water falling), telling Erin that she was a slut and a cunt, that she was Laurel's possession, her toy. But she still couldn't make herself come like she had that day; the drops were centered on her clit, not her cunt, and every thought she had was taking on their same simple rhythm.

Drip, drip, drip. A steady, inexorable pain. A dependable, maddening pleasure. There was nothing but the drops any more, nothing but this water falling on her. She was nothing but a clitoris being tortured. She was nothing but a stone being worn away by the rain. Erin thought about the stone she'd found on the beach one day. It had a hole in the middle that was obviously the work of water and time. Erin could vaguely remember (in a time before the water started) Laurel once telling her that she was no more and no less than what Laurel wanted her to be: "If I want to shove my fist inside you, you're a cunt for me to fuck. If I want to lend your mouth to a friend, you're one more possession of mine that I can lend to anyone I want. If I want to drip hot wax on you, you're a blank canvas. You will be what I make you, and you will learn that you are defined by my wishes and my desires."

Drip, drip, drip. The water would never stop. Erin suddenly felt her whole body go limp. It would never stop, because it had never started. She had been here her whole life. There was nothing and had never been anything but Erin-who-is-under-the-water-for-Laurel. The water defined everything, and the water fell at Laurel's command. Laurel made this rain fall on Erin because she wanted Erin to be rained upon. She wanted Erin to suffer (and, oh, was Erin suffering, endless pain as her body was worn down to nothing), and so Erin would do nothing but suffer.

Drip, drip, drip. And more. Drip, drip, drip. Water. Drip. Clit. Drip. Erin. Drip. Laurel. Drip. Breathe. Drip. In. Drip. Breathe. Out. Drip. Drip. Laurel. Drip. Whimper. Drip. Pain. Drip. Need. Drip. Want. Drip. Sob. Drip. Owner. Drip. Drip. Breathe. Drip. In. Breathe. Drip. Out. Drip. Nothing. Drip. Forever. Drip. Laurel. Drip. Breathe. Drip. In.

Nothing. The breath that Erin had drawn in remained in her lungs, and she felt herself go light-headed. Her whole body strained against the restraints as her clitoris sought the next drip. She could hear herself making a weird noise, almost like keening, and she hung, suspended on the moment, waiting for the next drop. And then...it came. Not a drop, but a hard, steady stream of water, and she screamed and ached and bucked and swore and came. And she kept coming as the water kept pounding down on her. She was drowning in it, and she couldn't stop coming although her clitoris burned and throbbed. It was like those times when Laurel held a vibrator there until Erin was coming continuously. This hurt the same way, but it was glorious in its awfulness.

When it stopped, Erin was a limp rag. She could feel Laurel unbuckling her restraints, but she had been passive for so long that moving didn't even occur to her. Hadn't the Owner told her (back at the beginning of time) to be still? She had no interest in talking. Hadn't the Owner told her to be silent? If Laurel, the Owner, wanted her to do anything, She would tell Erin to do it. Suddenly, there was the hard brush of something rough against her clit. Erin screamed and came hard. Then there was nothing for a while. Then another brush against her clit, this time the light touch of something smooth. Erin screamed and came again. Then there was something warm and soft, Laurel's tongue lapping delicately against Erin's clit, and once more, Erin screamed as she came.

After a short time, Erin felt Laurel's hands at her head, unfastening the blindfold. It was strange to feel the sensation of touch, because she'd really forgotten that any part of her body existed except for her clitoris. She kept her eyes closed and heard the indrawn breath just before Laurel spoke.

"You can move now, love."

Then Laurel's lips were coming down gently on Erin's forehead in the kiss that she always gave Erin when a scene was over and she was pleased with her girl. At that, Erin suddenly began to cry—deep, wrenching sobs that came from her center and washed over her like waves. Laurel climbed up on the table and pulled her into her arms.

"Good girl, goood girl," she crooned over and over. Finally Erin was all sobbed out and Laurel let go of her. "You can clean up later," Laurel said. "But now, I want you to come upstairs with me."

"Yes..." Erin began, amazed that her voice was still so shaky. She cleared her throat. "Yes, Laurel."

As they climbed the second flight of stairs that led to the bedroom, Laurel told Erin to stop. "Spread your legs and bend over."

"Yes, Laurel." Laurel gently brushed a finger over Erin's clit and Erin shrieked and clung to the banister, as she shuddered through another orgasm.

"This is going to be a fun evening," Laurel murmured.

Later that night, after Erin had cleaned the playroom and Laurel had made dinner, they sat in the living room and watched the fire that Erin had made. Every once in a while, Laurel would reach between Erin's legs and stroke Erin's sensitive clit, and Erin would come from the merest brush of sensation. When the first crack of thunder shook the old house, Laurel smiled. "Listen darling," she said gently. "Doesn't the rain sound nice as it hits the window?"

Even later, as they snuggled together in the big bed upstairs, Erin was jolted out of her light doze as Laurel touched her and made her come one more time. As she came down from the orgasm, she could hear the rain outside.

Drip, drip, drip.

Luck of the Dice

Jamie Gabriel

When I woke up that Friday morning in my sunny little apartment, a smile was playing across my lips. Sheila and I had a date planned for the evening. Stretching, I turned to lie on my back, and my hand wandered down my stomach. Mmmm. My eyes narrowed and I could almost feel the brush of her bush against my palm, the lips below hot with her silky wetness. Yeah, I knew just how I would tease her that evening to exact her plea for my services. Sheila was a challenging bottom. She had her pride, which meant I had to go to some lengths to make her beg, but it also made her eventual submission all the sweeter.

I rolled over and dialed the phone. "Hey Baby-doll, mornin'." "Mnnnh. Ryan?" Her voice was rough, and I could tell she was surprised, because I was never up before she was. Hah, good. I deepened my tone into one of brusque authority. "Come over tonight at nine P.M. Make sure you are dressed well for me; I want to see you in your black lace. From the time you arrive, you are not to make any requests unless they are first prefaced by 'Please, Mistress.' We will be playing a game. You are not to touch your pussy until given permission tonight. I want you good and hot for me, understand?" I took her silent pause as acquiescence. "Good. See you then. 'Bye, Babe." I hung up before she could ask any questions. I smiled again at the thought of her on edge today at work, perplexed and wondering what she was in for.

Of course I had plenty to think about, too. What would the rules be? Had to be a fun mixture of teasing, discipline, and only one or two chances for real gratification. That evening at the gym as I worked out, I listed them off in my mind:

2 - crop	7 - masturbate
3 - spanking	8 - take it in the ass
4 - pussy play	9 - tits
5 - kiss	10 - ride
6 - butt plug	11 - nipple clamps
	12 - fuck

At home I wrote them down on a piece of cardboard with a severe black marker. At the bottom, I wrote, "Each roll is two minutes, timed. Doubles gets double time."

I busied myself sprucing up my apartment while I thought about Sheila coming over. In her car, anticipating, wondering. Wearing the silk panties with the thick coarse seam rubbing between her legs. The rough lacy bra chafing her nipples. I knew she'd be hot for me before she even got here. What I loved about Sheila was that sex wasn't just a desire or a want for her; it was a need. Being topped turned her on like nothing else. She wanted to be taken, but she definitely didn't like to beg. I loved fucking her, and I got off on feeling her coming from my thrusts deep inside her. But as a top it was her submission that I really craved. So in a way, this game was its own kind of competition between us: who would hold out longer before giving the other what she wanted?

The doorbell rang and I checked the clock: nine P.M. Her careful punctuality pleased me, but I didn't let it show. She came in as I expected, head held high, an insolent glint in her eye. I didn't say anything, just let her walk into the middle of the room. Holding her with the look on my face, I made her stand there. I studied her admiringly. My, but she was gorgeous. Her Afro-Caribbean background gave her a lilting blend of features. Creamy, light-brown skin. Curly black hair in loose, shiny curls. Lips full and moist. Breasts ripe, heavy. Plump ass wide at the hips and perfectly round in back. She was wearing her black leather jacket, and a tight nylon miniskirt over fishnet stockings showed off the curve of her thighs. I could see one lacy bra strap peeking out from under her jacket, and I knew that she'd been careful to dress for me as instructed. Ahhh, yes.

She stood erect, looking straight ahead, but I could tell she'd noticed my tight blue tank top and my muscles still a bit pumped from the gym—I was getting buffed, not bad for a white girl, really—and she obviously liked what she saw. As I waited, her gaze traveled down to the sheen of my black spandex biker shorts and the bulge of my big cock hanging at my crotch. I saw a flicker in her eyes. With satisfaction, I heard the breath catch in her throat, saw a flush beginning at her cheeks. I moved in front of her, and unzipping her jacket, I gently slid it off her shoulders and down her arms. Underneath, she was wearing nothing but the black lace bra. Her naked brown skin was soft and warm, with almost a quiet glow in the candlelight. I liked the way her bra was tight with the weight of her full breasts, the lace reaching just far enough to cover her dark nipples. My own nipples hard and pricking through my tank top, I brushed up close.

"Tonight, Babycakes, your future will be decided by chance." I knelt to unzip her miniskirt, letting it fall to the ground. Her fishnet stockings came up only about six inches past her knees, leaving the rest of her thigh bare in front of me. I rapped the inside of her thigh sharply, and she shifted, parting her legs for me. I leaned forward, taking her in, my nose just an inch away from the curls of her dark thick bush visible through her lacy panties. Her chest was rising and falling more quickly now. I inhaled the rich scent of her pussy, so close in front of my face, its warmth almost palpable. Ordinarily I probably wouldn't be able to resist sliding my hand up along her stockings, stroking the bare insides of her thighs, slowing as I reached her panties, softly exploring that wet tangle underneath. But tonight I turned away abruptly, reaching for the rules placard.

I brought out the dice. "This is sort of a gambling game, kinda like strip poker. Ya feelin' lucky? Roll!" I looked sternly at the carpeted floor in front of us. Her brow creased in a question—or was it in irritation? I said nothing, and she slowly got down on her hands and knees in front of me, gave a quick shake, then cast the dice. "Awww, now, isn't that sweet? A two and a three, that makes five." Nodding toward the rules, I reached for the timer. "Baby gets to start off with a nice, simple kiss." I deliberately set the timer to exactly two minutes. Then turning swiftly toward her, I buried my fist in the hair at the back of her neck, and drawing her up to me I kissed her hard on the lips. Pushing into her mouth with my tongue, I felt her body straining against me, not wanting to give in too quickly—after all, she wasn't easy. But as I reached down, pulling her closer, spreading the cheeks of her ass with both hands, edging my thigh between hers, pulling the seam of her lace underwear up tight into her slit, she started to melt into me, wanting more of my body, harder against her. Suddenly, with a "ping," the timer went off, making us both start. Pulling away, I laughed. "Oh, I see it's time to stop." She looked at me in disbelief, ready to protest, but I just shook my head. "Nope, those are the rules: each roll gets two minutes. Roll again."

She tossed her head with a little snort, which said all too clearly, "I see what you're up to now," but I could tell she was also intrigued. Getting back down on one knee, she shook the dice. A five and a four: tits. I set the timer and moved behind her. Lips grazing her ear, I whispered, "Lucky again, I see, but how long will it hold?" Cupping her breasts, I worked my hands up under her bra. As I squeezed each nipple her back arched slightly, enough to bring her ass up against my cock. With her eyes half shut she let out a little moan as her head came back to rest on my shoulder. I could have stood there holding her like that, pinching and pulling her now stiff nipples, but my clit was starting to pulse, threatening to pull my hips into a thrust that would betray my excitement. Instead, I moved around to face her. Bending toward her, I pushed the lace aside with my tongue, and my lips edged over her nipple. "Dinnggg!" Damn. Why did I make that two-minute rule, anyway?

Through a clenched jaw I grunted, "Roll." I caught the hint of an impudent smile on Sheila's face before she turned away to drop the dice. But now it was my turn to smile. A one and a two. Three. That brat was going to get a spanking all right. I bent her down sharply over my knee, and the seam of her panties jerked up tightly into her crack, parting her for me. Whap! Whap, whap, whappp. My hand came down hard on her bare cheeks. After two more blows and with my hand tingling, I felt the heat rising on her reddened ass. Gently, I stroked her. Pulling her cheeks apart with one hand, I slid the other into her cleft, then pushed my thumb under her panties and down into her furry wetness. She shifted, spreading wider for me, but I pulled out quickly and struck again: whap, whap, whap. Arching in surprise, she made a noise—Was it a complaint? Before I could slap again to find out, the timer went off. "Hmmph—saved by the bell, huh?"

Sheila rolled again. Double fives: ride. Good. Now we're getting somewhere. Turning the timer to four minutes this time, I rolled my biker shorts down my legs, setting my hunky, thick cock waving in its newfound freedom. I lay down on my back on the bed, stroking lube onto its shaft. "Take off your panties, and get on top. You get a little ride. No hands. Put them up. Behind your head. Yeah. That's better." Sheila's breathing came faster and shallower as she slid her cunt onto my cock and pushed down to my abdomen, but with awesome restraint she kept quiet, riding me with long, deep thrusts, hands clasped behind her head. Her wet pussy's undulations were polishing my harness. With each stroke down I felt my cock bumping my clit, my harness strap chafed my asshole each time she made the return trip. It was almost too much to bear. A groan escaped me. In spite of myself I started to move. My clit, swollen to bursting, wanted more and more. Thankfully, before it could take over, the timer sounded. With a last powerful thrust I pushed her up off me and pulled my cock out. I knew I must be panting. Hot and irritated, I pulled my tank top off over my head, trying to look as unflustered as I could. Sheila showed a distinct smugness as she got up to roll the dice again.

With a little relief I saw that she had rolled a four and a two this time:

butt plug. Lady Luck was apparently smiling on me, too. I got out the plug and watched her while I slowly lubed it up. No sign of a break yet. This girl's tough. But I knew that her asshole was her secret weakness. I set the timer for two minutes, then told her to bend over. Sure enough, she did moan softly as I gently slid the plug into her ass. "Okay, now stand up straight, ah, ah—legs apart—now hold your plug like a good girl," I told her. Resolutely she stood up, butt clenched tightly, holding it in. Small goose bumps dotted her ass, and her nipples were hard little buttons. I moved in front, facing her. Letting my cock brush her bush, I reached around and began gently stroking and tickling her cheeks. Her muscles were taught, and she started to tremble as I kept teasing. She made a little sound in her throat. I started pulling, trying to pry her ass apart, but she managed to hold firm. I chuckled. "Oh, what a good girl." The timer sounded and immediately her ass went slack. I saw the plug starting to fall out and caught it before it landed on the floor. Maybe this laxity meant that she was indeed weakening.

Her next roll was a five and a six. Eleven: nipple clamps. Great! I needed some entertainment. Sheila loved to dance, and she sure was good at it. I tugged open the clasp of her bra and took it off. Sheila's full breasts swung gently, warm and heavy against my arm. Carefully screwing down the nipple clamps till they were very tight and attaching a two-ounce weight to each one, I explained that I was tired, in need of some rest and rejuvenation. Why didn't she do a little dance for her butch, hmmm? I flipped on the tape deck, then sat down on the couch in front of her. Luxuriously I let my hand reach up under my harness, and I lounged there stroking myself, while I looked expectantly up at Sheila. With pursed lips she began to sway for me. Every movement sent her tit ornaments jiggling on their own little dance. I liked this song because the beat built into a faster and faster tempo. Normally Sheila liked that too, but tonight it seemed to be an effort to keep up, and I could tell the weights bouncing and tugging at her nipples were driving her crazy. I laughed out loud, but then I took pity on her and stood up to take them off. She sighed with the release, and a murmured "thank-you" told me she was indeed softening.

When the timer sounded, she rolled again hastily, almost eagerly. A four and a five. I wasted no time; I had been wanting to get my mouth on her tits all evening. I pushed her down on the bed, sucking, biting, chewing first one nipple, then the other. They felt hot, their color deepened from the clamps, and I knew they must be tender with a heightened sensitivity. Sheila could come from nipple stimulation alone, and she was squirming beneath me now. I didn't think she'd be able to make it before the timer, but taking no chances, I let her nipples go and buried my face in her chest, inhaling her scent. I let my tongue lightly trace the bones of her sternum, enjoying the taste of her warm, salty-sweet skin. Moving back I gazed at her lying on my bed, her head thrown back, eyes closed, only her quick breath revealing the extent of her arousal. Glancing quickly at the timer, I squeezed her breasts together and drew my tongue slowly up the tight cleft of her cleavage and up further to her nipples, standing straight up, squeezed turgid. I sucked them both into my mouth at once and bit down hard again, holding them there for a few seconds, then released them slowly as the timer went off.

The next roll was a double four: in the ass. "Oh baby, you are in for it now. Your ass is going to get a fucking." I worked my big cock out of the harness, then slipped the little one into its place. Smiling as I set the timer for the full four minutes, I told her to get on her hands and knees on the bed in front of me. Lubing her exposed crack, I took my time, working the slick fluid around her asshole, then pressing my thumb firmly in, and oops, letting it slip quickly out again. By the time I started rubbing the tip of my little dildo up and down her crack, around her asshole, then squashing it into her anus, she was moaning out loud. I pushed all the way into her and grabbed her cheeks, spreading them wide till her crack was a flat surface jammed against my groin. Her head was down on the bed, her face shoved into my pillow. I leaned harder into her, and moving just my hips, thrust in and out and in again. Sheila's breaths were small, quick pants now. It seemed like her body was tensing involuntarily. Shit, was she really already about to come? Before I found out, the timer let off its relentless "ping!" She exhaled with almost a sob, and I thought I heard a muffled "no" coming from the direction of the pillow. Choosing to ignore it this time, I pressed the dice into her hand again.

Cruel luck. A one and a two: another spanking. Remembering that I still hadn't heard even one "please" for all my effort, I made her get back on her hands and knees. I let her wait there for a moment while I took off the harness and dildo and set the timer, then: Whap. Whap. Whap. Not a sound from Sheila. Thwap. My hand struck a little lower this time, smacking her squarely on the pussy. She gave a yelp and jumped. Ahhh, that was nice. "Spread your legs for me." She didn't move. Roughly I shoved her knees apart, then slapped her pussy again, then again, and again, in time to the rhythm of the music. My hand was getting slippery with her juices, but I knew my blows were stinging, and as I kept on she started to squirm and twist, grunting, trying to escape my hand. Abruptly, I stopped, then gently laid my hand over her hot mound, feeling her throbbing echoed in my own tingling palm.

This time when the timer sounded we didn't miss a beat. Silently, I handed her the dice. We both intently watched them roll. A three and a two: pussy play. I turned her onto her back and moved to lie on top of her. Pressing my naked skin against hers, I slid one finger between her lips. Sooo hot and wet and swollen. As I circled her clit, it swelled, poking up as if it were straining to meet my finger. I moved my hand down and slid a finger deep into her. Now she spread her legs willingly, clearly needing more. Was she ready to beg me? I fucked her slowly with my finger. Lying against the length of her body, I realized that my own cunt felt totally engorged, and I became aware that her thigh was clenched between my legs. She must feel me sliding against her, my own clit a tiny, hard rod, painting her skin with my juices. But she was moving with me now, pulsating around my finger. My hand moved steadily back and forth between her lips, and my clit fucked her thigh with the same rhythm. "Ding!" The timer surprised us both when it sounded this time. I rolled off her and she drew in her breath to say something. I glanced sharply at her, ready to savor my victory. But apparently she changed her mind, looking silently back at me. I gave her the dice.

Double six! Fuck! I put the big dildo back into the harness and strapped it on. Lubing my thick cock, I smiled at Sheila. "You want it?" "Yes." Her answer was a whisper. "Then ask your butch nicely for what you want, Baby. You know that's what good girls do." She hesitated. My clit was still stiff, and I felt it throbbing against the end of the dildo. I knew I was in danger of coming myself if I fucked her too hard, but I was determined to get the respect I deserved from her. I moved closer and deliberately started stroking the tip of my cock over her clit. This was too much for her. "Oh, please." "Please what?" "Please fuck me!" Good enough for now—and anyway I didn't think I could hold back any longer. I plunged into her, pumping hard once, twice, then shifted to a slower, teasing pace. In frustration, Sheila clutched at my ass, trying to push me deeper into her. But I had the leverage. Controlling my own mounting need for release, I stayed maddeningly slow, fucking her on and on, just one stroke per second. All four minutes ticked by and the timer finally went off. Before I could move, she murmured, "No, please. Please, Ry, don't take it out." "Mistress," I said, "say Mistress." She hesitated just a little too long. "Uh, Mmm, Mmmiss..." but I was already pulling out. She slumped back on the bed. I tried to give her the dice, but her hand remained limp. I curled her fingers around them, forcing her to take them. She looked up at me pleadingly, but I wouldn't budge. She had no choice. She wanted me in her. She wanted to get fucked. She *needed* to come. She had to roll again.

Without shaking them up she dropped the dice. I'll never know if she managed to do it on purpose, but somehow her roll was double six—again. "Fuckin' bitch." Well, I needed it, too. I shoved her down in front of me, then grabbed her hips and yanked her ass back up to meet me. I slammed into her from behind, and the impact sent a shock through me. Gritting my teeth, I took a deep breath, pulled my cock out a bit, and stopped. I reached around and took her clit between my two fingers. Gently I squeezed. "What do you want?" "Oh please, oh please, *please* fuck me." I eased the cock deeper into her and was met with a moan. I started to fuck her again, a little faster this time than before. Sheila was panting hard now. She was almost over the edge. My own clit was pounding. I felt like it was getting larger and larger. I couldn't ignore it anymore. I moved faster, harder, not caring anymore that Sheila was about to come and I still hadn't gotten my prize. But then she spoke again. "Please, oh please," in time to my thrusts, "please Mistressss-ahh!" The end of the word trailed off into a cry, and I could feel her coming, spasms shuddering through her body from her cunt to her ass, through her stomach and chest and up her back. Her head turning from one side to the other and back. Her legs crossed and uncrossed, her thighs squeezing together around my cock inside of her. Not knowing whether it was this full-body response or Sheila's submission that put me over the edge, and not caring, I felt my cunt clenching, and warmth radiating through me from the end of the cock smashed against my clit. I thrust inside of her again and again, all of my attention focused on that one point, the meeting of my cock and my clit. Distantly I heard the timer ringing its overtime warning, unattended.

This time I didn't stop. After all, you can't *always* play by the rules.

The Body in Relation

Deborah L. Repplier

Vee stance, Salutation, Sink, Salutation. The surety of each move, the rhythm of my body strong with itself. *Vee stance, Salutation, Sink, Salutation.* Through the open window of the chapel, crab apple rises on the breeze, wafts in reminding it is May. Early May. I watch the instructor dressed in black, her body fluid, each move water pouring from a vase. She circles around the five of us, eager, awkward students. My dance card empty. She circles around and calls the steps, watching as we move through the beginning level.

I, at the beginning level. Two years later from you. I seek the balance in my body, in my life. Marvel at my two hands, open-palmed, before me. Fingers tight and fingers splayed. In T'ai Chi Ch'uan, it is the Yin and the Yang. The duality of life. The wanting and the not wanting. And the body in relation. The instructor starts at the front of the room, facing the wall, her back to us. At her neck, her dark hair tapers into a vee. *Vee stance.* Vee.

(You in your white blouse, after a shower and your hair in a vee.)

Her hair is not sweaty, although she removes her over-shirt and stands before us in black. Sculpted biceps emerge from her short sleeves, already tan this May.

Outside, the city traffic, a siren in the distance, the wonder of a mockingbird in this city. (I live in this city now.) Inside, the choir practices in the room beneath us, chords rise through the marble floor, gyrate in the air as I swing my hips. My legs are firm from rollerblading, my weight balanced. *Horse.* And my hips sway with gyration, vibration. I notice the instructor notice my hips in gyration. She averts her gaze quickly, but not before I recognize the look in her dark eyes. Duality. I feel it in my own sometimes, my body sticky with sweat, passing young dykes on the corner, by the train station. I rollerblade the bike path to pass by, my hips swaying above well-defined legs. Look them full in the eyes; I don't look away. I don't look away from the instructor now although she wants me to, I can tell. Her Yin to my Yang.

She wears silver bands on both hands. Her middle fingers are crooked, I notice, when she stands before me to adjust my arms. She avoids my eyes until she is through touching me. When her hands drop and my arms are correctly positioned, she looks at me before turning to the next student. Meets my eyes. *Salutation.* This goes on for weeks, but each week, I notice, she lingers a bit longer, praising my grace. Her hand adjusts my wrist, slips lightly up my bare arm. The Yin and the Yang between us. The wanting and the not wanting. She meets my gaze silently, holds it as she moves away. The mockingbird. The siren. The choir. The look in my own eyes. I tell her I may not be able to make class next week, I have late business outside of the city.

(I live in this city now.)

"Come," she says. "Come late and I'll stay after class with you; we'll make up what you miss."

(I miss you. I miss the pain of your hands squeezing the flesh of my shoulders, the wall pressing hard against my back as your knee pushes my legs wide. Still I miss you.)

Late and in work clothes: T'ai Chi in short skirt, black nyloned feet. Jacket and heels tossed to the corner. *Separate, Withdraw, Push, Drop. Separate, Withdraw, Push, Drop.* We have become a class of three now. A gay man, a straight woman, and myself. And the instructor. The straight woman stands in front of me and I mimic her movements. Fluidity is something only inside of me now. The instructor comes to me (open), demonstrates what she wants me to do.

"Do it for me," she says. Scent of sandalwood between us, her hands on my waist, squaring my hips, my shoulders. A current runs through me at her touch; my nipples pierce the lace of my bra, strain through the silk tee. I focus on the piano in the corner, the vase of irises on top, knowing if I meet her gaze I will stumble. I startle myself (beginning level).

"You need to work on the new steps," she says. And the others close the door behind them as they leave. She demonstrates once more what she wants me to do. This time her eyes do not leave mine, even when her body turns away. This time when I feel her hands against my skin, I do not try to control my quickening breath. The wanting. The not wanting. We stand in the center of the room; ahead the piano with its narrow strip of mirror sends our midriffs back. I see her fingers on my waist, crooked fingers, her black cotton peeking from behind my blue silk. She presses herself against me, her breasts against my back, her taut nipples matching my own. In the piano mirror her hands across my torso. And tighter. Tighter. Deep breathing.

"Don't forget to breathe," her tongue flicks my left ear. Lingering chills. Her warm breath.

In the mirror, I watch her hands glide over the fabric of my breasts, watch and feel my nipples pinched, straining through the silk. Gasping, I collapse against her. In the mirror, her left hand disappears. She is searching for something. I feel my skirt rise, her knee between mine from behind. *Horse. Lift and open.* Ankle. Wrist and reach. Her hand against me, searching. I feel her lips flit across my neck, biting, sucking my flesh. In the mirror, her right hand slips under my silk tee and pushes my bra aside. Fingers moving beneath fabric. My nipple on fire. My knees forgetting their strength. The mockingbird's incessant courtship call. And the choir.

I turn away from the mirror.

(This road away from you begun.)

I turn to the instructor, learning. Leaning into her: press my mouth over hers encircle her body in my arms. Who is gasping now? My hands slip under her T-shirt. My fingers define the bones of her back. Trace the bones, slowly. Then hard.

"The door is unlocked," she tells me, her fingers pushing aside the crotch of my panties.

"Lock it." And my hips rise to her.

"No," she says. "I can't. Even if I could, the sextons have a key."

Her finger inside me, thrusting. The scent of sex, sandalwood, our sweat, the crab apple. The taste of her lips.

"Take me in the bathroom," I plead, and we walk, me backward and oh her finger inside me, the endless distance to the door: one animal, four legs.

Block and Grab, Press, Roll, Separate. Block and Grab, Press, Roll, Separate. The tumblers click in the lock and she turns to me. I know that look in her eyes. I know the look in my own right now, although I cannot see the mirror. She lifts the silk above my head and I am before her in my black lace bra. Her mouth moves to mine. The lace forced away, exposing my right breast. Her lips claim territory from my lips to my nipple. Her teeth send sharp gusts of pleasure-pain. The duality.

(My breasts untouched until...I live in this city now.)

Her hands yank, my skirt lifts, my thighs push wide. Both hands. Breathing. Breathing. Sandalwood. Sex. She is searching. Her mouth is on my nipple. Her eyes never leave mine. My hips are gyrating and I can tell she likes it, although she is not watching. My legs are wide but she does not enter me. She rubs me, pressing, rubbing, parting. She pours liquid fire into my body.

"Please," I moan, my hands pulling wrapping pushing her arm against me. Begging, please.

She cups my cunt, moving the flat of her wrist against my clit. I am open and wet and empty. She steps back, lifts my skirt to look.

"Hey," her hand moves to the virgin tattoo on my hip. "Blue hummingbird," she smiles at her discovery.

The counter is cold against my ass. Her tongue insistent, again. I feel her pelvis, black jeans rubbing between my legs. I lift her T-shirt over her head, freeing her nipples beneath. Silver hoops. My hands open palms against her flesh. Fingers splayed. Tug and oh. *Press, Roll, Separate.* Gasp and gasp. Her hand to my cunt, again.

"Please," I beg.

"Please what?" she whispers back. Ohhh and fuck.

"Please fuck me, *now*." (I live in this city now.)

Her mouth into mine. Her tongue. Her fingers into my cunt, to her knuckles.

"I'm married," she says, turning inside of me, her fingers gyrating, untwisting me. "I'm married."

(We were married too.)

Her hand is hard. Hard and then nothing. Empty ache. She slips her fingers to her lips, sucking, tasting me on herself. Slips one to my mouth.

"Should I stop?"

NO and NO and NO. She rewards me with her hand. "Shhhssshh," she cautions, "The sextons will hear us."

"Oh God," I gasp, her Yang to my Yin. "Oh God, how many?" I want to know. *Lift and open. Wrist and reach.* Three she tells me. "And your wife?" She rewards me with another finger. "Please." My mouth so dry, my tongue barely moves across my lips, my body empty, aching, searching. Still not enough.

Wrist and reach. Wrist and reach.

And in that moment, she gives me all of herself.

Push, Drop...Single whip, Adjust. Push, Drop...Single whip, Adjust. Beginning level.

The surety of each move:
water pouring from a vase
my hips gyrating
her hand seeking the wanting
the not wanting
sandalwood sex...the rhythm of my body in relation
strong.

All of herself in that moment. Enough.

When He Was Mary

Heather L. Seggel

Once upon a time, there was something in her that called out directly to my cunt and said open-open-open as if it were a department store on sale day. She was the salty sweat-tang of the Pacific, my California girl. When we fucked, I took her whole fist in me and I would rock and squeal and squirm, open, open, open to her, and mostly I would look into her coffee-brown eyes and say, "Oh, girl, oh, my girl," her hunger feeding my own until we would both die from excitement and I'd curl myself around her, still shuddering in orgasm, and kiss the back of her neck, pressing my smile into her. I was in love, her little steamed dumpling, needed and content.

So how come I don't like it now that she's a man?

Don't assume—it's not the cock issue, even though all my friends insist it is. All he really got was a bigger clit, and that's just more for me to love. It's like a Malibu Barbie dick. And I do love it. At least in theory I do.

When he was Mary, I wanted to live between her thighs. Her cunt was the sweetest thing I'd ever tasted. I ate her clit like a last meal and held her hips while she bucked into my face. I drank from her and made her weep and wail. She actually screamed with pleasure. I could have eaten her forever. My Mary. My girl.

Now, it's so many things. He can't seem to settle on a name. "Call me Jack, no, Phillip—no, do I look like an Alex? Try Alex." And he's so fastidious now. Last night, I felt him run the duster over me while I was sleeping. I wonder if his final surgery will involve implanting a squeegee in his arm. He asked me to call him Gunther this week. My Gunther, my surfer dude. I started to cry, and he used Lemon Pledge where my tears landed on the coffee table.

I fell in love with Mary at the beach, at a bonfire party full of drama-fucks with goatees. We volunteered to make a beer run, and walking up to her truck she'd stop every few steps to look at some strange treasure visible only to her in the sand. She picked up a broken sand dollar with more care than I would have thought possible and studied it as if it might contain the secret of life. If she looked at me that way, I thought, I might turn to gold. I brushed her shoulder.

"What would you do if you found me out here in the sand?" I asked, washed in shame and embarrassment the second the words were out. I held her gaze, though, and waited for her to laugh. Instead, her face grew thoughtful.

"You? Well, first I'd need to look you over," and her hands were there, right on my shoulders, turning me so gently I almost burst into tears. She turned me so my back was to her, then ran her hands down my sides, resting them lightly on my hips and drawing me to her. My body was singing sweet gospel. I felt her breath on my shoulder.

"Then I'd need to sniff you—to make sure you're fresh." She giggled, but then her lips were grazing my neck as she breathed in, sending words like hot and wet into my bloodstream, taking my soul with her. We didn't even kiss on the mouth that night, but we never made it back to the party.

The next morning, she brought me coffee and some daisies she'd picked herself, with obvious care.

He spent most of this week at the gym, snapping towels at other men's asses, looking at his own ass in the mirror and comparing notes. Guy stuff. He asked me if I'd mind if he grew a goatee. "They can do it with hormones or hair plugs," he said, "like Elton John has." My little Elton Artfuck. I go into the bathroom, so I can cry over the sink.

She was my earthy whore when I loved her. Now he says, "Suck it," and looks away. He gets off on it, though, and he still comes like a girl, all fierce but soft underneath. Still vulnerable. My sweet thing. It's now, when I'm pinning him down, licking the length of his shaft and pushing the hood back with my tongue, that it feels like old times. I run my thumbs over his nipples—Mary was an A-cup, so he hasn't bothered with any reductions yet—and watch him struggle with how good it feels. It feels good to me, too, to see him like this. I take his entire dick in my mouth and tell myself it is a dick, and yes, my girlfriend is a man, but instead of freaking out I am becoming more turned on, I think because he *does* look so beautiful right now, squirming and filling my mouth with that sharp secret taste. I run my hands all over him, teasing his curves, making him moan, thinking, my man, oh, my man. And something hidden deep in me is breaking up, a lifetime of theory converting into ragged need.

"Honey," I say, taking a deep breath and hoping many things at once. "Honey, I need you to fuck me. Now."

He is turned on by what I'm saying, but it's obvious I'm not being clear. "I want you inside me." And this time I dip down and lick his length once more, to illustrate my point.

He sits up and looks at me like he is from Mars and I am from Venus. My heart is thudding in my ears, the soundtrack to my brain, which is chanting fuck me fuck me faggot boyfriend girlfriend lover lover lover fuck me now. We are facing each other, and I never noticed what a strong jaw he has until now, and before that thought can get far he has grabbed my shoulders and pinned me to the bed and Lord help me Lesbian Feminist Collective but I am spreading for a man, and just thinking that is making me come. He has to push hard on me to get his cock between my labia, and the pressure is making me come harder, and he slides up until the tip strokes my clit on one side and now the other, and I am a slut, and I am a whore, and I am divine.

When he was Mary there were easier ways to define things, even though nothing was ever simple between us. But we never did the things, or could have conceived of the things, we did last night. After our marathon, I made strong coffee and we stayed up the rest of the night talking, like old friends, which we are. And when we finally settled down for an early-morning nap I wrapped myself around him and kissed the back of his neck for luck, leaving my smile-print on his skin.

Wishbone

Chrystos

for Burning Cloud

I want you slick
between my thighs hard intent so
greedy as if being inside me deep is
all you've ever wanted
until your hunger catches
me screaming for you to push us
out of time
Want your womancock
following my every clenching gasp
want you to throw open my soul
Keep you safe in
Want your need to be in me
until we're soaking shameless wet
Your butch hands gripping my ass
shaking going hard
I want to wish
baby that you'll never
take your bone
out of me

from **Box 309**

Jane DeLynn

Not just the outer but the inner door was unlocked, as they often are in crummy tenements.

I walked up the stairs, six-pack in hand, metal indented from decades of footsteps, walls bumpy from ancient attempts to make interesting the "texture," the paint chipped, graffitied, peeling, names of old lovers *(Mike & Cathy forever, Julio loves Sandy)* etched by key or knife into its surface. Garlic, marijuana, fried chicken, rotting food—Spanish music and kids screaming and TV for the various constituencies mingling in a way that was pleasantly familiar. In the past I had known buildings like this so well, with their geographically labeled (NE, SE, NW, SW) apartments, their bags of garbage (brown bag inside plastic) tied up outside the doors, the forgotten joys of downward mobility, whether involuntary or chosen.

I went up the stairs as far as I could, until I faced a metal door to the roof. This location alarmed me.

Feeling stupid, but following instructions, I shut my eyes, albeit I could raise the lids slightly and see through my eyelashes. I shifted from foot to foot, then leaned with my back against the iron railing, which I rolled against to work out my muscles. Finally I sat down, and despite my intense curiosity and nervousness my mind began wandering until I almost fell asleep, as I have upon occasion in a dentist's chair.

"Are your eyes shut?" a voice startled me.

"Yes," I half-lied, my heart pounding as if I had been caught doing something forbidden.

"You're supposed to be standing. Get up, but keep your back toward me and your eyes shut if you don't want to be sent home." A bit awkwardly, for I was feeling dizzy, I pushed myself to my feet.

"Move forward, so you're not leaning on anything."

I did. "Okay. Now reach out with your left hand, backward, until you feel the banister."

The cool railing felt good in my hand, though my sweat made me grip even harder.

BOX 309 **93**

"Good. Now move to your right...more...more...*Stop*. The stairs are right behind you. A few more inches." I shuffled my feet very slowly until I could feel my heel sliding off the edge of the step. "Good. Now walk down. Slowly."

"Backward?"

"Yes."

"I can't." I was petrified, afraid I'd fall into the void, or that she'd push me (even though her voice was below me.)

"Of course you can. You just feel with your foot until the step disappears, then lower yourself very carefully. Don't worry. I'll be there if you fall."

I let my left hand slide slightly down the railing, whose knobbiness (from decades of paint?) I was now grateful for, as it helped anchor my hand.

"What about the beer?"

"You won't need it."

"Are you sure?"

She said nothing. I reached out my right hand but could not touch the wall.

Finally, ever so carefully, I moved my right leg down onto the next step. Then my left.

Still proceeding cautiously, but slightly faster, like a child learning to walk, I backed my way downstairs.

I heard a click and felt, rather than saw, a darker blackness.

"One more step," she said. I lowered my foot—then a tremendous jarring went through my body, as my foot found, not space and a step, but a solid floor. As I was getting myself together, she slipped something over my eyes, with elastic behind my head. Fur: a material I recognized from far-off days of semi-interesting sex.

She spun me around, so that her voice was in front of me. "What do I look like?"

I opened my eyes, but it was as if I had not. "I don't know."

"Good."

"Why? So you are ugly!"

She laughed. She took me by the hand. She pushed my left shoulder, she pulled my right, and I began to turn around. Then she told me to spin around myself, until she said to stop. I got dizzy first.

"Okay." She took my hand and began to lead me. Remembering the step, I resisted.

"Where are we going?"

"You'll...see."

"Will I?"

"Don't you trust me?"

"I don't know."

"Then what are you doing here?" I tried to figure out which way I was facing, but the spinning and walking backward had confused me. I liked the sound of her voice, though, which was husky, as if she were thirsty, as if she were getting a cold, as if she had talked too much all day.

We stopped, I heard a slight creak (a door being pushed open), then, after she warned me to lift my foot a little, my foot landed on a somewhat softer and more absorbent surface, which I realized was wood.

I felt wind, I heard a kind of aching sigh, I heard the click as she turned the lock on the door.

"No," she said, grabbing my arm, for I had reached for the blindfold. Her fingers felt strong. At first I liked it, but then I felt cornered, and I grabbed at her like a cat.

She pulled my hands away and pressed them to my sides. I pushed up as hard as I could, but though I work out, I couldn't get anywhere. I heard her chuckle. Finally, I stopped trying.

"Promise not to try to take the blindfold off?" she said in an amused tone.

"Yes."

She let go. I stood there, my heart pounding, panting from fear—and, I admit, excitement. My breathing sounded loud in my ears, like my grandmother's used to when she slept in my room. At the time it had made me want to kill her.

"Can I sit down?" I asked, less to sit than to do something to cover up my loud breathing.

She didn't say anything. I waited awhile, then asked her again. Still silence. Had she left the room? I crossed my left leg behind my right and began the process of lowering myself to the floor, which was much more difficult than you'd imagine without visual cues.

"Don't do anything unless I tell you."

I stood awhile more. Sweat was emanating from me, not from one particular place but in a kind of suffused oozing. The floor creaked.

"What's your name?" she asked.

"Chris."

"Chris *what?*"

BOX 309   **95**

"I don't want to say."

"Is Chris your real name?"

"No," I admitted.

"What's your real name?" I was silent.

"Oh, you're one of *those,*" she said. "You'll learn soon enough." A long pause. "Chris," she said, exaggerating the Chris, "it's warm in here, don't you think?"

I shrugged. "It's okay."

"Well, I'm warm." Pause. "Would you like to take off your shirt?"

"Uh. Sure."

I began unbuttoning my shirt. As I had never worn this shirt before, I had trouble getting the buttons out of the button holes, which made me self-conscious (lest she think I was nervous), so I tried to move faster, which made me more clumsy. Finally, I got it off. Not wanting to discard it, I held it in my left hand. How much did it weigh? Six ounces?

I was conscious of my erect nipples.

"Drop it."

"It's...clean." (I didn't want to say "new.")

Snicker. I let go. "No bra."

"No. I...I used to be small. Not that I'm big now, exactly, but I keep forgetting."

"You forget?" She sounded incredulous.

"In the store I mean. I haven't bought a bra in...so long."

"I see..."

What did she see? Oddly, I felt almost sleepy.

"You work out?"

"Yes."

"Where?"

She continued questioning me in this calm and impersonal manner, as if at a doctor's office. The calmness was reassuring, though it gave me the feeling she was disappointed in my appearance. But perhaps she was merely nervous about how I'd feel about hers.

I could both hear and feel the floor move as she approached. Her breath sent little waves of warm air at my face, waves that must have smelled nice, since they did not repel me. I smelled armpit smell too, not so nice, but that could have been me.

I waited, but she did not touch me. If she had, perhaps I would not have begun to get wet.

"Can I take the blindfold off now?"

"No."

"When can I?"

She moved away, with her breath and warmth. "Please finish getting undressed."

Please: What did that mean? I didn't know the rules. Would she say, in the same neutral voice, please bend over so I can shove a dildo up your butt?

Slowly I unbuckled my brown leather belt, unbuttoned the top of my shorts, unzipped the zipper. The shorts began to slip off me, and I held them so they wouldn't.

"Let go," she said.

As my right hand let go, my shorts tilted and I heard my keys drop out. I restrained an intense urge to pick them up.

"What's the problem?" The fingertips of my left hand still clutched my shorts.

I didn't want to put the idea of running off with my clothing into her head, if it was not there already. "I've never done anything like this before," I finally said.

"You've never taken off your shorts in front of another woman?"

"You know what I mean."

"Do I?"

We were silent awhile. The ticking—was it my watch? "I...I'm scared," I said.

"Of course." Silence. "What are you most frightened of?"

"I don't know."

"I'm sure you do."

"Being hurt, I guess," I finally said. But that wasn't it, exactly.

"Chris." She said it reproachfully, almost sadly. "You do know that some of the things we might do together might hurt you, don't you? That's partly why you're here, isn't it?" she said in an insinuating fashion.

"Now let go of those shorts, and take off your underpants too."

This was difficult, as I could not raise my foot to take my sandal off with my shorts around my ankles. Nor could I kick the sandals off. When I tried to bend I got dizzy. Finally I had to sit down, pull off the sandals, and then remove the underpants.

"This is really embarrassing," I said, then stood up.

"The little femme," she said, I suppose in honor of the lacy black under-pants I had bought from Victoria's Secret in honor of our "date."

"I'm not sure what I am," I replied.

"Perhaps we'll find out."

I was now barefoot and naked, my hands over my breasts. For all I

BOX 309   **97**

knew, the windows were wide open, and people in the apartments across the street could see me.

"Turn around so I can see the rest of you. Slowly."

As I turned I felt awkward and unattractive, the parody of a model.

"Move your legs apart."

I did this slowly, as the gunk was creating a suction between my thighs. It made a slight noise as it broke, which I hoped she could not hear.

"My, my," she said. Very lightly I felt her fingers brush the hair around my vagina, or rather (as hair has no feeling), I felt the pressure of the hair moving the follicles. Then it seemed to stop, although I felt (or thought I felt) the warmth of her hand above my skin. At times I can be aroused by anything, and I felt gunk moving down my legs. Moving slightly, as if to shift weight, I moved my legs farther apart, willing not just her fingers but her hand inside. Instead, she moved her hand and ran her fingers down my face. With the light breeze (open window? fan?) the gunk dried into a mask.

If I was excited (and I was!) it was not so much because of what was happening as because it reminded me of something I had seen in a porno movie. The predictability of my response—as if I were your standard male voyeur—irritated me.

She stuck her fingers in my mouth.

"Do you like to taste yourself?"

I shrugged. "'Sokay."

"Just okay?" She moved her fingers in my mouth until the soapiness was gone, then returned them to where they had been before.

"Keep them apart," she commanded. I had started, or perhaps had just started to think about, contracting my legs around her hand.

"God," I said. "Oh God."

"Surely you're not going to come," she said.

"*Jesus.*"

Jesus. I bit my lip. I was dripping. I haven't felt like this before, went through my mind, though of course it wasn't true. I wanted to howl. I was moaning. She withdrew her hand.

"God, please don't stop," I begged.

"*Don't,*" she said. "I don't want you to."

"I can't help it. Oh God..." I grabbed her hand and tried to shove it in my vagina. "*Please.*"

She grabbed my left arm and twisted it behind my back. I fell onto her, felt her solid muscle.

"Who makes the rules around here?"

She turned me so my back was toward her. Her right hand moved around my body to grab my right nipple. She squeezed it between her thumb and finger. At first the pressure felt good, because the pain distracted me from my desire, then the pain itself became the problem. "Ow," I said. "Ow...ow." She put her left hand around my neck and yanked. My feet slipped and I was leaning against her, her body supporting me. Once I stopped fighting this I relaxed and let myself sink into the pain. The pain was so deep it was no longer connected to the nipple but spread in waves. But somehow it didn't matter. Then she began twisting her hand, and the pain was again sharp and discrete, as if a pin were going through the center of my nipple. I became worried, not about the pain, but that she might do permanent damage to my nipple.

As I tried to pull away, she grabbed my left nipple with her left hand. This fresh pain distracted me from the old one. Then she squeezed more sharply with her right hand and the lower part of my torso twisted in that direction. Soon this alternation of pain became a rhythm, and I again relaxed.

At that moment she dropped my right nipple, grabbed my hair, pulled my head back, and sucked, really hard, on the side of my neck. It would be a gigantic hickey. Then it became a bite. I felt like she was eating me. Like she was an animal. "Ow. Oh. Ow." Her teeth dug into me. What if she drew blood? Wasn't she worried about AIDS?

She stopped for a minute. She pulled back my hair, so my throat was exposed to her.

I wanted her to bite it, suck my blood, make me part of that strange race.

She pulled my hair harder. "So, Chris, does it matter what I look like?"

"No."

BOX 309   99

Clubs

Kim Yaged

"It's good to see you around again," Mrs. Mitchell peered over the rim of her oh-so-fashionable sunglasses. "We were all hoping you'd make it back to the club this summer. There were rumors that you might not."

"Thanks," Erin's eyes wandered. "I appreciate you saying that."

Bikinied and lying in her lounge chair, Mrs. Mitchell, housewife, mother of two, looked better than she ought to. "You look good," Mrs. Mitchell observed.

"Gosh, Mrs. Mitchell, you're so full of compliments." Erin shifted her weight from side to side. She was glad to have the sunburn on her fair skin to veil her blushing.

Mrs. Mitchell stared into Erin's roaming eyes. "Is something the matter?"

"Oh, of course not." Erin was able to momentarily focus her gaze on Mrs. Mitchell. Mrs. Mitchell leaned forward and reached for her tanning lotion, her breasts straining to be released from the narrow confines of her bikini top.

"My boss's wife, mother of two, boss's wife, mother of two." The reality of it struck a redundant cord in Erin's mind whenever she was presented with the name, the thought, the person. Mrs. Stephanie Mitchell: thirty-five, wife of Dale Mitchell, thirty-seven, mother of two, Jared, age ten, and Karen, age seven.

She was hot, Erin repeatedly reminded herself. She is hot. Long, wavy blonde hair, inviting blue eyes, a body that even Erin's college work-outaholic friends would envy. No one could have resisted her.

"You'll have to come over some time and do some more work at the house," Mrs. Mitchell interrupted Erin's thoughts. "I can't tell you how many compliments I've gotten. Everyone at the club was talking."

"Great." Erin dug her hands deep into her pockets. Alone at Mrs. Mitchell's house. Alone. Her mom had played golf with Mrs. Mitchell the next morning.

"I'm sure the kids would love to see you."

Her husband was Erin's boss.

"I don't think we should do this," Erin had said as she pulled her head away.

"No one's home," Mrs. Mitchell consoled as she enveloped Erin's ambivalent body in her arms.

Their lips touched once more and Erin felt the weight of the woman pressing her into a linoleum kitchen floor. Mrs. Mitchell's hips felt wider than her figure revealed and her skin pulled not so taut. But there was an aroma to her flesh that became the focal point.

Boss's wife, mother of two. Boss's wife, mother of two.

That's when the incantation first inaugurated itself, but at that point, it wasn't forceful enough to stop her. Erin stared at the pile of her clothing lying beside her while Mrs. Mitchell removed what little remained of her own.

Wife, mother of two.

When they were naked and inside each other, their scents combined. Erin had worried about being able to remember what to do, but she need not have bothered. Mrs. Mitchell's knowing hands guided Erin across both their bodies to the coarse mound of hair between her thighs.

"Touch me like this."

Erin's hand rested awkwardly between Mrs. Mitchell's thighs as Mrs. Mitchell reached for Erin's clitoris and began massaging it, the same way Erin had sometimes seen her fingering the straw in the name-brand spring water she sipped while sitting by the pool at the club.

Wife, mother, she tried to tell herself.

Erin's hips began moving to the pressure of Mrs. Mitchell's fingers. She could feel her own wetness stream down the crack in her behind. She pushed Mrs. Mitchell's hand away and pressed her vagina against Mrs. Mitchell's, squeezing her own breasts in frantic abandon.

Mother! Erin's mind screamed.

Their hips beat faster, forming bruises. Erin wanted to taste the mixture of fluids rubbing between them but lacked either the nerve or the composure to do so. There was nowhere for her to look. She wanted to sink her teeth into Mrs. Mitchell's shoulder. She wanted everything.

"Excuse me?" Mrs. Mitchell peered up at Erin from her lounge chair.

"I'm sorry. Did you say something?" Erin shook the confusing memory out of her mind.

"I just asked if you are enjoying school."

"Yeah," Erin shook her head in confirmation. "I am."

"Of course," Mrs. Mitchell lay back down on her lounge chair. Her gaze no longer locked on Erin's. "Are you seeing anyone?"

"Yeah," Erin nodded.

"Of course." Mrs. Mitchell leaned over and lifted her glass of club soda to her lips, concentrating as she sipped from the straw.

"As a matter of fact—"

"Erin!" A call from across the pool interrupted. Erin and Mrs. Mitchell looked up simultaneously to see a semiflushed Kate rapidly approaching. Her short, light-brown hair was already beginning to go blonde in the summer sun, her flesh darkening in equal proportion.

"There's some confusion over at the Halfway concerning shifts," Kate addressed Erin once she was within hearing distance. Erin ran the Halfway House, the refreshment stand on the ninth hole.

"I'm sorry." Mrs. Mitchell interjected. "I don't think I've had the pleasure of your acquaintance."

"Kate Reynolds," Kate extended her hand. Mrs. Mitchell hesitated before reaching out to Kate, moving her arm in a meager up and down motion.

"Mrs. Dale Mitchell," Mrs. Mitchell replied, then turned to Erin for further identifying information concerning Kate.

"Uh, Kate's one of my housemates at school," Erin fumbled. "She's spending the summer with us and working at the Halfway House. She'll probably help with other odds and ends as well."

"Uh-huh." Mrs. Mitchell nodded as though she were beginning to understand something. "Right."

"Well, I've got to get back over there," Kate motioned to the Halfway House. "It was nice meeting you, Mrs. Mitchell."

"The same," Mrs. Mitchell contributed unenthusiastically.

As Kate began walking away, Mrs. Mitchell examined her firm, round buttocks, which curved into slim, muscular thighs, then looked up at Erin, who was apparently doing the same.

"Uh, Kate," Mrs. Mitchell hissed through semiclenched teeth. Kate turned to face her. "Since Erin has to rush back to the Halfway House, maybe you could help me for a moment."

"Of course," Kate was reticent.

Mrs. Mitchell gazed up at Erin with an expression that seemed to command, "You're dismissed."

"I'll see you back over there, Kate." Erin obeyed the unspoken order and turned and left.

Mrs. Mitchell leaned over and flashed her bosom at Kate in somewhat the same manner she had done for Erin earlier.

"What is it I can do for you?" Kate spoke in an overdone sugary tone of condescension that the less informed mistake for politeness.

"Tell me about Erin." Mrs. Mitchell reached her arm back and massaged her own neck.

"What would you like to know?" Kate spoke in a businesslike fashion.

"I'm concerned about her. Her mother and I are very close. You do know that?" Mrs. Mitchell squinted her eyes like a cat looking into the sun.

"Yes. So, then, surely there's nothing you don't know about her." Kate wasn't enjoying this game as much as she pretended.

"You're right," Mrs. Mitchell smiled ridiculously. "But of course. I just wanted to make sure she's happy."

"Happy?"

"Why, yes," Mrs. Mitchell appeared confused. "What's so odd about that?"

"Nothing—nothing at all is odd about that."

There was a pause.

"Is there anything else?" Kate inquired.

"No, Kate, that is all. You may go."

Veiling her contempt, Kate turned to leave, then stopped. "Oh, by the way," Kate faced Mrs. Mitchell as she spoke, "I'm happy too."

Erin was the only one still at the Halfway House when Kate returned. She leaned on the counter of the service window waiting for customers that didn't come.

"Did you work out the schedule?" Kate asked as she walked in through the side door.

"Yeah, not too many casualties either," Erin smiled.

Kate sat down beneath the ledge of the service window in a spot where no one looking into the Halfway House could see her. Her face aligned with Erin's crotch.

"What are you doing?" Erin laughed but didn't move away.

Kate undid the button on Erin's shorts, then the zipper. She wiggled Erin's shorts down to her hips and stared at Erin's vagina.

"What's going on down there?"

"If you're ever with that woman again, I'll kill you." Kate spoke plainly. Then she leaned forward and placed a soft kiss on Erin right where her vulva began to part.

"Let's close this place up," Erin said. "We've got things to do at home."

Kate leaned forward and with her tongue parted the pungent lips of flesh facing her as she spoke into Erin's insides. "This can't wait until home."

Sour

Kathe Izzo

Tonight I am everything
and you are my first love
curled now   suckling
yummy girl   apple of my eye

the girl I own like a mother owns her baby
with her eyes and her shoulders and the dusk
of her body   the tongue with which she licks that baby awake
inside the deep folds of neck traced with dinner crumbs
and salty sweet blue powder beads of dreaming

I rub my face in you deep like sugar
like blankets left on some street corner
in the box cut open like a door

I have known you since the beginning
I ate cereal from your hands

It was 1969 and you were just being born
I was big already I was eleven I was growing everyone seemed
to notice
I let boy after boy touch my body   underwater
on the railroad tracks   in stuffy living rooms
on rainy afternoons   five different ones telling me
what they wanted to do   my body black like butter in their hands
curviness out of control   lips pulled back

Every once in a while there was a boy
with a sour smell beneath the buzz
a smell I could count on coming in from way ahead
like it could be any boy but it was you
that smell from inside behind the sweetness of your mouth

like when I was almost twelve it was as if I was being pinned down
by your breath
   lifting my ass when I was only fourteen to your baby girl lips
   hundreds of miles away   lying in your cradle   or no   maybe
     a little bigger
   in your backyard mourning over chickens killed for dinner

   I have been smelling you everywhere
   face down in my own lap
   in the garden   fingernails full of dirt

   Crazy how it turns now when the sour comes home
   my handful   my darling
   all grown up face down in wet metal
   car in the lot sun still going down wrangly boy gone haywire me
   I am up your ass   ain't no mama here now   baby girl
   knows how to drive a car   better get that butt home soon
   curve in my hand   come on

   something like changing a diaper   legs curled up in the air
   I will never leave you alone   like cats curled up
   in tall summer grass   with long tongue
   I will clean you up till you can clean yourself

   If there is some way I am separate from you
   you better prove it cause the way I see it   I see it in you

   baby girl apple of my eye

Unfinished Business:
Five Vignettes of Never-Consummated Lust

Bonnie J. Morris

There is a room where lost loves wait, the ones who said No, or who said Yes once and not a second time; the ones whose eyes and arms led me to believe I had a chance, and about whom I spun sweat-deep fantasies; this sex that I never had, or had only in my own mind, was some of the best. It had some greatness to it.

All the women in this chorus of my longing and desire had their own rotation of individual stardom and performance on my stage, their mildest gestures thrilling, their informed consent to my unconsummated wanting of no moral consequence at the time. Now I leaf through my old journals and watch past crushes leaping off each page. Oh, yes, *her, that one*—embarrassed pronouns and pronunciations, surely. Some of the fiercest lost erotica spelled out in my own hand: *the ones that got away.*

I. 1978: I am a vulnerable demimonde.

At sixteen I play the role of a Paris streetwalker in a local community theater production of *Irma La Douce.* My best friend and I, eleventh graders hoping to act professionally, are cast in this "mature" musical on condition that we be mentally and morally prepared to enact adult sexual themes. My crush on my best friend is not lost on our voyeuristic director, who brilliantly and/or sadistically casts us as lesbians: I play a young prostitute, and my friend is the tough dyke pimp who keeps me as her lover. Through this construction we become, onstage, a lesbian couple. My friend is horrified. I am thrilled, grateful, overwhelmed—and closeted.

Night after night in rehearsals and performances it happens this way: my blonde beloved recoiling from the idea that women might love women, but rallying to the challenge of *acting;* me, silently grateful to the director who freely orders me to touch and be touched by the girl I long for hourly. Background roles, really, our staged flirtation; the adolescent lesbianism a mere afterthought in the panorama of street stereotypes, the private drama barely noticed by our cast members, all laboring to pull together an ungainly production on a deadline; but for me a nightly agony and bliss of being *directed* to have my honest desire shine through. Sitting pretty on my beloved's lap, smelling her Jontue cologne, she giving me a cool appraising look with what she thinks approximates butch panache. "Now, this may make you both uncomfortable," the director begins with each new staging, instructing me to look at my partner as though I wanted her—and I do. I am asked, in the name of community theater aesthetics, to hold her hand, stroke her leg, let my fingers linger on her thigh, and be her femme, me in a tight split skirt and she in pants playing the role of procurer. We are sixteen.

I come home from rehearsal each night and dream of sex, barely able to confide in my ever-present journal the actual lesbian urges I feel toward this girl; I change her name to a male pseudonym in all my desperate poetry. Yet I envision, constantly, what woman-to-woman lovemaking might be, imagine her coming into my room and roughly initiating me. Yes, I want her to take the upper hand, so to speak, to show me in private all the cruel affection of her narrowed eyes onstage. Overpower me. Make me beg. Turn me over. Pin me down. I call her by her male name and write our initials in my homework, during the school day before I report to the theater (and my awaiting role as her lesbian lover). Does anyone know I am feeling these things, at school?

Backstage, on the eve of my seventeenth birthday, I am applying makeup to my face when she comes up behind me, sings out "Happy birthday!" and suddenly kisses me. I am seated at a mirror and thus see my own face reflected as her lips bury richly in my neck. I watch my features crumple with desire, that this touch of hers, so careless, so removed from the street sexuality she enacts toward me onstage, can make me swoon so deeply. On the table before us is a small jar of creamy peanut butter intended for the cast party buffet later on; but now she unscrews the jar and breaks the virgin surface with a plastic knife, writing to me "I LOVE YOU." I keep this jar, uneaten, for weeks, looking into the gradually cream-blurred edges of her throwaway declaration, as one might gaze into the depths of a pool.

Onstage, opening night, an audience of our schoolmates, teachers, and parents watches her touch me precisely with possessive gestures crafted for the show. I feel hot stage lights wreak the tobacco scent from her fingers; my entire being focuses on the waves radiating from my solar plexus as she rests her costumed arm on my shoulder. This public affection, this exhibitionism of our fantasy fierceness as lovers, played out before a paying crowd!—and yet, in reality, she is straight, tuned out to my own queerdom. The observers congratulate us on our acting.

Every night after rehearsals or performances we drive the southern back roads in her old Cutlass Supreme, drinking wine and smoking dope, but her boyfriend is the driver and I'm stuck in the backseat watching them kiss. I'm in the backseat, dying, at sixteen, because she is sleeping with this boyfriend, the preacher's son, and not with me; they let me tag along. One night the boyfriend drives us home when she is drunk, half-sleeping; she leans her front car seat as far back as its lever permits until her wild blonde head is resting in my lap. She grabs my little finger and locks it in her own and sighs, "I love you, girl." The wind rushes over our bodies and I am stupefied with wanting, unable to move; the boyfriend, like everyone else that year, is oblivious to my closeted desire. Now we are not on that stage positioned as lesbian lovers for the sake of art; the boyfriend's eyes are on the road and she is dazed, her head between my legs. Now my hands descend from their numb pausing, and I trace my beloved's face and hair, and she is acquiescent, singing.

I am sixteen and this is how I live: honors student at a private school by day and lesbian actress by night. I tell nobody about these things.

II. 1980: I am the mirror to my own desire.

Two years later I am enrolled in a summer performing arts academy, still training to be a professional actress, just turned nineteen and now proudly out as a lesbian—but still lacking any sexual experience with a woman. In my acting class at the university is a smoldering Jewish girl, generally regarded as Broadway-bound by her jealous classmates; the prize, the star, deep of breast and dark of eye, and somehow I am partnered with her for morning warm-ups. This one knows I like her.

"All right then: mirror exercise," calls our tired instructor, bidding us pair up and synchronize in that timeworn mime training routine where one person begins slow motions and the other copies her exactly, as the reflection. I stand in my damp leotard and tap shoes and move as my partner moves, to mimic her exactly—but she's not going to be conventional, this one. She looks at me and starts to stroke her own breast, slowly. And nods at me to follow.

Well, then, I stroke my own. I am the mirror, after all. I must do as she does—just reflecting—but what is going on here, after all? She can choose to make me touch myself. So is *she* touching *me?* She looks at me as though I were a mirror, a long one in her private bedroom where she can make love to herself, vainglorious. She puts her hair this way and that, sighs, and holds her face, her collarbone, letting her hand slide across her breasts again. I am following, hot with public sweat, the invitation to touch her vicariously spilling over into the possibility that she is stroking me—or, at least, coolly commanding me to stroke myself. She is embracing herself—I hold myself, in turn—and her. Across this separate space, this wicked girl puts me through the motions of exactly how I'd touch her and makes me rub my own breasts until my nipples rise erect. I am feeling her touch her own creamy sloping cleavage through my hand, the hand she pushes through me, our bodies paired and stroking. And just like that, it's over. The class applauds enthusiastically.

III. 1981: I am dancing in the middle of the circle.

Still a college sophomore, still nineteen, I'm in love with three different women and have at long last fucked one of them, but it's this elusive dance major I really want, the one who insists she's straight as an arrow while rolling up the sleeves of my feminist T-shirt with her languid, bony hands. She has sleepy, drugged eyes, cinnamon-colored hair, a hip and tranquil interest in everything; smitten, I drag her to a women's bar I know where we have a certain privacy but no dance floor, and of course she wants not intimacy but dancing. She tells me there's another place. I follow.

Suddenly I'm inside a four-story gay male disco where there are no women but us, and at first they won't let us in. I'm a teenager, underage, stamped with marks to show I can't drink alcohol, my college I.D. and passport riffled by the bouncer, but the dance major leads me swiftly through room after room of cruising men and buys my liquor for me, until by the time we reach the top floor I'm slopped with gin and tonic. There at the top is a frantic loft with skylights cracked to let out heat, and bearded men throbbing to disco. "Come *on*," she says, and looks at me, appraisingly; I like to dance, but I'm repressed, a bookworm.

She reaches out and slips her long hands into my hair, finds the catch in my tortoiseshell hair clip, and in one gesture undoes it and flings the barrette behind the bar. She brings down my braided hair and fluffs it out intently. Then she pulls me into the middle of the dancing men, who obligingly part and form a circle around us, watching, clapping, urging us on.

I dance with her, jumping. When we tire, we move together, closer, and I get to see her face that near—she reaches out and turns me, holds me from behind, and rocks me in her arms while the men shout. I heat up like an iron, gasping as I feel her pressed behind me. Her pelvis cups my ass and our mutual body heat flickers right there in the erogenous forge; if we were paper dolls we'd be burned up now, red ashes. Careful, now, the men are watching. But I know exactly what my face looks like: the same look of unexpected satiation that I saw in the makeup mirror on the eve of my seventeenth birthday. Here it is, the dancer cradling me into her black velour sweatshirt, holding my head, and I'm melting into the floor, the flesh swooning off my hopeful teenage bones. And the gay men are all smiling.

When I tell her how turned on I am, and proposition her at last, she says No, I Love You Madly As a Friend, but then takes the silver Navajo bracelet from her wrist and puts it on mine. Later I hear that she got into freebasing cocaine and was last seen hitchhiking west toward Colorado, and I never find her again, although I look and look. I wear that silver bracelet to this day, and I hope that she's alive.

IV. 1989: When I want a Jewish woman again.

For years all my lovers are Jews, like me; all of them, until I'm twenty-two. Then I go off to graduate school for my Ph.D., and for six long years none of them are Jews. I love one Catholic or Protestant or Russian Orthodox or Maronite Christian dyke after another; Germans, Italians, Arabs. Some of them know very little about Jewish culture; one lights her long brown cigarillo on my Shabbos candle.

When I need to be with a Jewish woman again I find this one—who's involved with someone else and won't give me the time of day, or even admit that she is a lesbian at all—so maddening and teasing that I do anything to get her attention, including lying naked on her dining room table in a game of strip poker I lose to her and her lover. The two of them admire me; the one I want runs a Bic pen between my legs, her own writing hand and writing instrument briefly and directly connecting with my lust in a gesture of sheer grad student spontaneity. Stoned, I'm lost in my own fantasy.

In this fantasy I am making love to her Jewishness through mine. Here we are, women from the same tribe, tracing our bloodlines back to Egypt, where our dark foremothers cut brick for Pharaoh. Her pomegranate breast rolls out of the Sinai and into this dream. I see her Jewish face in mine, a lantern I can walk by. In bed we could be survivors, descendants, ancestors. Her history would tell my own in a long and supple kiss. I would know her in all the spices of the Promised Land, weighed and measured temptingly. Her carob eyes, her chocolate hair, her pale brown skin like cinnamon, her ginger voice, her nutmeg laugh, her smoky taste like hazelnuts, like chicory, like cardamom. I am a merchant trading spice; I am a gardener of delights. Let me shake the tree to make the spices fall; let me rub the nut husks to make the shells glow; let me grind the spice for seasoning and see that it is good.

She is a compass to the Middle East: the savory sheen on her skin, this set table, this celebration. I want to be her Sabbath Queen, come through her window on Friday night bearing myself and full of bearing, caught, big and laughing, over the kitchen embers, leaving her blessings where she can find them, if she's been good and even regardless.

She disappoints me by saying No, and I move on to other Jewish women: three, four, five of them as lovers, all sublime. I don't forget the one who briefly touched me with her pen.

V. Undated: I dream about her.

Love at first sight and I'm old enough to know better, neither a teenager nor a student any more; but I know what I like and how to make the ladies moan, by now, if I can get a chance. This one I want to do everything to: throw her down on a futon and eat my way to China, for example, or have her surrender to me in any number of delightful ways, but I tell myself that kissing would be enough. That "all" I want to do is kiss her. And this is a nicely packaged lie, because now I'm too experienced with women.

The problem with the kiss is that while one's face is soaking in the soft exchange of tongues, one's right thigh takes on a life of its own and goes panning for gold way ahead of permission. That right thigh wanders deeply and soon becomes embedded between The Other's legs, and then the right femur searchingly moves upward and teases out the dampness through the jeans. Then the hip bone slides up and down and plunges at an angle as the tongue is plunging, the right leg sliding like an arrow, knee to pelvis, and in this way her kneecap, rigid from my motion, fits my vulva like a soft inverted bowl, and soon someone is shifting—she is, I am. When I say that a kiss would be enough, my right leg laughs at me.

This one is swaggeringly handsome, after all, swaggeringly lovely, knows her stuff, and I become a brazen suitor offering her a drag off our joint, which is almost gone. "No matter," I say, holding the hot inch to her lips; "Just finish it. Go on. Burn me."

We are not lovers. The reasons why don't matter. What matters is my constant dream-drama with this dyke: in my sleep I swoop off trees, drive across islands, and storm through tunnels to win her hand, a sort of medieval fairy tale of proving my worth in feats of exhausted passion. During the waking day, when I run into her, I marvel that she doesn't know how busy I've been in the night saving her ass and then fucking her brains out with my writing hand, the hand that writes the dream down, later on. The writing hand loves describing this dream girl but wants more, wants breasts, wants clitoris, wants contractions and not ink making a mess on the page. Come on, I'm not afraid of you; burn me. But no. We are not lovers.

I watch her face, fingers, legs, hair; everything moves and thus can be remembered—in the dream. In the dream I climb out of the bath, rosy in face and fortune, bend to towel her legs dry and wait as she combs her hair; I pull on soft and faded clothes, amble barefoot over worn wood planks, and let myself land like a marlin on the surface of her bed, my damp limbs sprawled akimbo laughing, and I pull her down to kiss her glad eyes with my open mouth. In the dream she begs me not to stop, and I turn her over, rub her back until she melts with comfort, and I look at her beneath me and think of animals living peaceably inside their taut and furry skins. I think of touch that is both wild and tamed. How shall we play, who shall we be? We imagine ourselves as horses, grazing and galloping across her bed; she is horse and I am loving rider. I groom her carefully, brushing and combing her entire body from end to end. Feel this massage; I love you, proud creature; you don't scare me. Don't move, until my brushing hands clear and heat the last of you. I ride her hard and put her away wet.

Then I become the goddess who wears her hair as it was in childhood, long for braiding, and she takes great flowing strands of it and wraps it between her breasts, between her legs, braiding me into her until my scalp prickles with desire. My hair stands on end for her, alive, alert to her noble distance, her amused proximity. Pull me to you. Reel me in. Wrap me up. And eat me.

I dream these scenes, and I see her in my sleep. When I'm awake we don't speak of such things.

At thirty-five I've had most girls I've wanted; these five I didn't have. It doesn't matter where they are today, or why I never saw them with their shirts off, never touched them anywhere besides, perhaps, the face. They lit a spark in me, these five, and the sex I had with them in my own mind could rival even some I really had. I look with open eyes at these lost loves and tell them, "Burn me."

from Missing You

Peggy Munson

There is no human nicotine patch.

So, I stand here, smoking the imaginary fingers that would have been your hands, almost tasting the clove of your breath, tightly rolling the last scraps of you in paper, licking the edge of it, and sealing the cylinder. I stand here, choked up in the clear air. I am sick of being able to see across the room without your lithe, white obstruction. You would kill me for comparing you to a cigarette. You always hated it when I smoked and now, now that you're gone, I'm cursing you for not allowing me a single addiction.

That is, but you, of course. I'm addicted to you.

Since you left, I've cut out all the pictures of your magazine ads, the ones with the tampon box underneath, and pasted them on my walls like Anne Frank did with her pictures of celebrities. And much of the time, I live like Anne Frank, making noise only at night when I stroke and open myself like a nocturnal flower. On some nights I go out and fearlessly scavenge for others like you. But there are no others like you. I've looked long and hard. You are one of a kind. Those ridiculous eyebrows plucked into a state of perpetual wonder, your pouty girl lips, the unobtrusive breasts that merely suggest the bane of womanhood, fallopian tunnels to invisible cities. That's why they chose you for the ads, and that's why I chose you.

But of course, as we now know, you were the one who chose me. You chose me from the beginning, very deliberately.

The first thing you did when we committed to each other was to put me in your will. You made allusions to hereditary diseases, to the fact that blood is unpredictable and spills out and overflows the vessel, becoming a moat between lovers. You made allusions to people who wanted you gone. It was all very strange and scary to me but I just said, I'll protect you, and I planned to. And you helped me in the planning.

Then I put you in my will, of course, because you said there was no harm in planning and you had a lawyer who was good and cheap and would do it on the spot. I left you everything. I would have deeded my soul to you, had you been any more of the devil. But I couldn't, and you weren't, and it would have been easier, in some ways, if you were. I left you my collections, which were all I had of exceptional value, and my stock certificates, and my life insurance. I even went to the extreme of writing you a letter to read after my death, proclaiming my love for you.

This all felt very exciting to me. I felt like we were political prisoners in a world that didn't understand people like us. I believed they were out to get you, as you said, and I would have to marshall my forces of protection.

I began preparing for the inevitable.

I didn't want to buy any serious weapons, because people might begin to wonder and ask questions. I did start collecting knives, though, first from those TV ads, then from Williams-Sonoma and the cooking department at Macy's. I had sharpeners, too. I stored the knives in a special drawer and kept them sharp and occasionally tested their ability to break flesh by cutting the tops of my arms, or the bottoms of my feet. I began to like the feeling of walking on the cuts. A feeling akin to walking on sharp rocks on the first barefoot days of summer, a reminder of frailty, and of freedom.

One day you caught me doing it, but you didn't stop me. You just said, through your pouty lips, *Can I watch?*

You didn't wait for an answer. You drew up very close to where I was sitting on the kitchen floor, and I became quite aware of you sitting there, and how close I felt to you right then. I desperately wanted to impress you. I held the small knife firmly and deliberately and pulled it over my foot and made a cut in the padding. Then you gasped, your lips parted slightly, your eyes grew big, and you said to me, *I want to taste it.*

Since we had both been tested and didn't have the virus and everything you said excited me, I just exhaled, *Okay,* and guided your head down.

You moved your tongue very slowly around the tip of each of my toes, letting the blood gather and bead on the pad, and when it was running down my foot in a thin line, you moved your tongue slowly to the spot beneath where it was flowing, then up the line to the cut and back again. Then you sucked on it, and licked, and sucked. You sat up and the blood dribbled over the side of your mouth like misapplied lipstick and you licked it clean and swallowed hard and said to me, *It's not enough.*

Excuse me? I replied.

I want more, you said a little louder. Then you held me down the way you do and let your hair drop down so it brushed against my breasts. You rolled me over onto my stomach, then sat on my back and held me there with the full force of your body. I could feel your knees squeezing into me, as if you were riding bareback. I could feel the way they seemed to be directing my blood upward and downward, to my head and between my legs, until I felt almost delirious.

In retrospect, I wondered how many times you had done this. I wondered how you knew all the places that would bleed so effortlessly, taking longer to clot, even with small incisions. I wondered how many turkeys you had carved.

But at the time, I was impressed by your workmanship, a rare thing in these times. I expected you to excavate in obvious places, but you surprised me by starting with my ear, drawing the knife slowly over the small arc at the top. It was so close to my eardrums I thought I could hear the skin splitting, a sound like paper unfolding. The blood it produced was splendid—red, gushing, full. It wouldn't stop for minutes, just kept pouring out as your ravenous sounds were amplified there, like a baby suckling a microphone. You wanted me to hear it this loud. You knew what it would do to me.

When you finished on one side, you grabbed my hair and held my head down so that the ear you had cut was pressed into the kitchen tile, and I felt a throbbing there and wondered if I was leaving a puddle, but the pressure you exerted seemed to act as a poultice. For a moment, you set the knife down right in front of my eyes, with the tip pointed to the space between them, and you began grinding your hips into my body until I felt heady from the blood loss and the pressure. For a moment I blacked out, and when I awakened your fingers were stroking the knife in front of me, almost like you were giving it a hand job, and a single drop of blood was beaded on the tip, and you said to me, *Stick out your tongue,* and I did and you wiped the blade clean.

My own blood tasted salty and slightly metallic. It wasn't the gravelly blood I remembered from when I was a kid. It tasted the way I imagined caviar would, if I had lived a different life, if I hadn't given you everything.

Afterward, you talked about cultures who still believed in bloodletting. I did feel better. I felt pure and clean, and healed of something I can't explain. I knew it was something that had always been there, and I knew somewhere deep inside of my cells, it was still reproducing. It had to do with my excesses. I knew I would need more of your handiwork.

This is what they never tell you about vampires. How some people, once their blood is taken, can't cross over to the other side. How there is a limbo, a dependency, an addiction that develops. How some of us, despite ourselves, have too much life in our veins, and it becomes an impediment, chokes the traffic of our thoughts, and makes us too hungry, and wanting. They never tell you what this does to a person. The never tell you how the skin dams up the blood inside, causing a pressure, an energy, that is almost unbearable.

I feel it now. I am pacing. I wonder where you are.

I go to the only shrine to you that's available, the Menstrual History Museum. I used to make this pilgrimage even when you were still around, to remind me of who you were and what we were: unique. The museum enshrines a historical collection of female products like those horrible thick strap-on pads the size of industrial sponges; products designed to cover up, to shame, women's blood.

It is all I have of you now, except the pictures, since you took everything when you went away.

This month, the museum is highlighting recent menstrual history, showing how far we still haven't come, kitschy advertisements implying tampons alone will overthrow the patriarchy. There are ads of women jogging, playing tennis, talking about freedom like we've finally won our revolution. Many of them wear white, the color no girl dares to wear for years, despite her virginity, because it is a display board for shame. In the middle of these ads is one of yours, blown up to poster size, the Mao of menstruation. Your lips look overfed and ripe. But primarily, you suggest containment—a girl who would never take the biggest portion of anything.

Of course, I know differently. I know how you would often want more than I could give you. How my cells tried to replicate what you had taken, moving single file through my capillaries like red bowls on an assembly line. Bowls to fill with food for starving children, because somewhere, children could be dying for the slow replication of bowls.

This is the kind of world you taught me existed. I never knew. I wanted it to be just the two of us, frankly. I wanted us to form a circle. I wanted the world to be you.

And I believed, foolishly, that you needed me. That we were two rare blood types sharing a transfusion. That I was keeping you alive, as you were me. That you wanted to get closer to my heart. I didn't realize how easy it must be to find others like me, others needing to be cut open to be healed. I admit, some days I wanted you to completely devour me, bowl by bowl.

I miss you.

A week after you left I read in the paper that leeches are being used again for cleaning wounds. What the article didn't mention was internal wounds, the marks left when someone you love has abandoned you and you have to move through the world alone. I move slowly, like a leech, believing I am not good for healing anything, just for scavenging.

Sometimes when I miss you I start scratching at myself, like an animal clawing at the walls of a cage, until I bleed. On the days I have no Kleenex I lick myself, and taste the salty taste, and swallow it back down. But it remains mine; it is not the same as you doing it to me. I still want you, and need you, to take away the parts of me that are too much for one person to be.

One day I bleed in front of your picture, compulsively scratching my skin as if I were allergic to what I am. I look down and a thin streak of blood is sliding down my arm. It tickles. I have nothing to clean myself with, and I don't want anyone to know what I've done. I'm afraid to ask the curator for a bandage, and besides, she would probably only have tampons or menstrual pads, too large and bold for such a small embarrassment. I unroll my black sleeve slowly down over the blood. I know it will stick. But now, the blood tickles me underneath, feeling much like a caress.

Of course, I should have seen signs, but I didn't. The only signs I ever noticed were the ones that said Stop. You had me so fixated on these that I didn't notice the others, the colors you were cultivating in private, roads of yellow brick, fields of green. I had always associated you so much with the one. Everyone had, because of the ads. You were the woman in red, the little red dress that was, and wasn't. The little red dress outside and inside. The exposed and the hidden. The wanted.

And I guess that's why you had to leave. Because of being wanted. You were too full of, and too representative of, things they wanted.

I go to the museum all the time, because it is the only way I can imagine your face.

The museum is free, but I always give a donation, sometimes change I find on the way over, sometimes all the money in my wallet. I stand in front of your picture. I remember you holding me down, the things you did. I want to be with you now.

Some days, and this is what keeps me coming back, I imagine you will be displayed here in the flesh. Even though it goes against logic, I imagine you will be here. As any addict knows, addiction is like a love affair. And as any lover knows, touch only brings addiction to the surface, causes panic in the streets of the body, makes one hunger for more.

Ridin' Bitch

Toni Amato

Nick Sergeant kicked shut the front door of her trailer and dropped her jacket onto the couch. She sat down and held her head cradled in her hands, then ran them through her thick black hair and wiped them along the thigh of her jeans.

"I gotta stop putting so much shit in my hair."

The only thing that kept her cowlicks from turning her into a dyke Howdy Doodie was handfuls of Dippity Doo. It made her hair greasy and slick and left a stain on her pillow that reminded her of her father, but then, how often did Howdy Doodie get laid?

Eight o'clock on Monday morning. Another weekend bender. Feeling like one of those chewed-up presents the cat kept leaving at the front door, Nick aimed the remote at her television and started a fresh pot of coffee. Eight hours to go before she had to get to work, cooking short order at Jimmy's All Night Cafe. If she was lucky, she'd grab a few hours' sleep between now and then. But first she had to clean herself up.

Nick poured a cup of black coffee and walked down to her small bathroom. In the mirror she assessed the weekend's damage. She was starting to show the signs of too much drinking and tomcatting. Stroking the lines around her mouth, she crinkled her eyes in pleasure, thinking that the creases made her look more like Bogart.

She sat on the toilet and pulled off her engineer boots as the water ran into the tub. In the thick steam, she slowly undressed. Beneath her white oxford she wore a cotton undershirt over her small breasts. She unzipped her chaps, revealing gray button-fly jeans with a rude, shiny stain around the crotch, the snaps gummed with lube. It had been a rough trade weekend, like they always were. She only undressed when she was alone in her bathroom.

She ran her hand down the thick patch of hair running from her belly button to her pubic bone, which throbbed from the thumping of the base of her cock. Deep lines were bitten into her ass cheeks where the harness had been snapped tight. She set the sticky dildo on the edge of the sink.

"I'll clean you up when I get out of the tub, big guy."

After Nick had stripped down and carefully folded her clothes, she lowered herself into the hot water and lit a cigarette. She leaned back, closed her eyes, and as the bath water rose over her breasts, sleepily recalled last night's conquest.

Olive's was beginning to fill up with the late-night dance crowd. Butches in black jeans and collared shirts crowded around the bar. On the dance floor, girls moved slinkily with their partners or worked it for the women they wanted. Nick sat at a table in the back, rolling cigarettes and drinking shots of Jack Daniels. In the pulsing light of the dance floor, only her white shirt showed, almost electric blue from the deep black of her vest and chaps. She sat with her long legs stretched out, boots crossed, and watched the crowd.

Her game was to guess which girl would fall for the butch sitting quietly in the corner. Nick considered herself a one-woman stud service, her only rule this: that the girl be the one to propose they go home together. She didn't chase tail. It came to her, preferably wagging.

Up on a platform above the dance floor was Chi-Chi, the bar's go-go dancer, doing the bump and grind, her image projected in stop action on screens around the club walls. Nick felt a slow heat rise up in her belly as she watched Chi-Chi's back arch, thrusting her hips and breasts forward, tight against her clothes. Nick would have sworn on a stack of Playboys that her cock was growing longer and harder, straining the frayed seams of her crotch.

"Quite a piece, huh?" Steve, the bar's faggot owner, put a fresh drink on Nick's table. He glanced up at Chi-Chi, then slapped Nick's cheek. "Bet you wouldn't mind a little of that action."

She pulled her legs in and leaned forward so Steve could hear her over the music. "No, I sure as shit wouldn't. But a piece that sweet's gotta already be taken."

"No, Honey. She just dumped some dagger she was with. If you hadn't left with that bit of trash so early last night, you would have caught the whole thing." Steve pulled up a chair and sat down, more eager to dish up dirt than to pour drinks.

"She wasn't trash, Steve. She was a nice young woman in need of a little companionship." Nick lit the menthol Steve held up expectantly.

"Always a gentleman, huh Nick?" He pulled a drag and held his cigarette near his head, palm up. A real Grande Dame. "You call it companionship? I call it the nasty, Honey. And you keep the local drug store open in lube sales alone."

"Alright, Steve." Nick waved a hand at him. "But what about Chi-Chi and her ex?" She had tried to sound nonchalant, but Steve's eyes lit up conspiratorially.

"Girl, was that ever a cat fight! Her girl started in with some noise about other butches checking her out and getting crazy jealous. Chi-Chi told her it was just a job and to chill out. Well, before I knew it, Chi-Chi threw a drink in her face and told her that she'd had it with paying the bills for some piece of shit that couldn't even mess up her sheets." Steve shrieked and slapped Nick again, this time on her thigh.

"Huh. So she's alone tonight?"

"Yeah. Maybe you can show her how to wreck a bed, Nick." Steve rose and waved toward Chi-Chi. "Bon voyage, darling, I have to get my pretty little ass back to work."

Alone at her table again, Nick spent the evening with her hand on her thigh, watching Chi-Chi dance and waiting for her shift to end. A few times women came over and offered her a dance, but her eyes riveted on the platform communicated other plans.

At last, an hour before closing, Chi-Chi's miniskirt rode up to a dark shadow between her legs as she climbed down the ladder from the platform, and Nick remembered the boys in high school who had put mirrors on the soles of their boots so that they could see up girls' skirts. She sat up a little straighter and watched Chi-Chi work her way across the dance floor to collect her pay.

Her sequined shirt shot sparks across the room and her platinum blonde hair gleamed in the lights. Nick admired the shelf of her ass as she balanced over the bar to talk to Steve, who counted out twenty-dollar bills. They spoke for a few moments, then Steve poured out a shot of whiskey and nodded toward Nick's corner.

"Thanks, Steve," she thought and belted back the last of her old drink. She shifted her legs and concentrated on rolling another cigarette as she watched Chi-Chi from beneath lowered eyelids. A minute later, long fingers with painted nails placed a drink on her table.

"Mind if I sit at your table? All the others are taken, and my feet are killing me." Chi-Chi bent over, the fabric of her skirt spreading taut across a firm dancer's ass, then stood up, smiling. On her finger she twirled a five-inch spiked, sling-back heel.

Nick stretched her arm over to pull out Steve's empty chair. "Go ahead. Thanks for the drink." She lit the cigarette Chi-Chi held tilted between her dark red lips, then licked her own closed and stuck it behind her ear. "You dance real well."

Chi-Chi smiled again, then frowned, her lips puckering into a small pout. "Thanks. Too well, I guess. My ex had a real problem with it." She looked off across the dance floor, slowly emptying now as women paired off and passed through the curtained front door, either huddled close in quiet whispers or boisterously joshing with departing friends.

Nick glanced quickly at the dancer's face. Chi-Chi's green eyes rimmed with tears, and Nick thought how she would look with a different sort of pout, an entirely otherwise earned set of tears.

"So I hear. Tough luck, huh?"

Chi-Chi stubbed out the half-smoked butt in one complete and vicious twist. "Nah. She was useless, anyway." She took a drink of her rum and coke, prints of her full mouth lingering on the tumbler. "You don't dance much, do you?"

"I think there are better ways to get to know a girl than dancing." Nick pulled her smoke from her ear and lit it, letting the blue cloud escape in a slow stream from her lips.

Chi-Chi laughed, tossing her bangs back from her face. "What's your name?"

"Nick. Nick Sergeant. And your name is Chi-Chi." She extended a large, square hand studded with heavy silver rings. "Nice to meet you."

"Nice to meet you, too, Nick Sergeant." Chi-Chi curled her mouth into the sarcasm of a smile. "Your mother didn't give you that name, did she?"

"My mother didn't give me shit. It's as good a name as any. Did your mother name you Chi-Chi?" Nick tilted back in her chair, one arm draped over the backrest.

"No, Steve did. It's as good a name as any."

"I'll drink to that." They lifted their glasses together and Nick's wrists ached at the sight of Chi-Chi's breasts, rising and shaking with the motion of the dancer's arm. Chi-Chi set her drink down and ran a nail around the rim in slow, deliberate circles.

"So...how do you get to know a girl, Nick Who Doesn't Dance?"

Nick answered through a lopsided leer. "The civilized way. Over drinks. Someplace quiet."

"Someplace quiet." Chi-Chi took a lipstick out of her purse and licked her lips, parting them slightly for the mirror she held up. "My place is quiet."

"What about your ex?" Nick finished her drink and placed the glass squarely, carefully on the table.

Chi-Chi snapped the compact shut and rolled her lips together. "Who cares? She's history." She put a hand over Nick's, still wrapped around the shot glass. "Come home with me, Nick. We can discuss civilization over Grand Marnier."

Nick stood and helped Chi-Chi into her leopard skin coat, then eased her own heavy black leather jacket around her shoulders. The dancer turned to her and slipped several fingers through the steel cock ring on the left epaulet.

"I like your accessories."

Outside Olive's, the wind blew Chi-Chi's hair back as they stood beside Nick's Triumph. With one hand on the bike's gleaming gold gas tank, Nick asked, "How'd you get to work, Chi-Chi?"

"I caught a cab. The car belonged to my ex. I got the apartment, she got the jalopy." She threw one long leg over the seat of the bike and leaned forward, her elbows on the handlebars. Her open coat showed her cleavage above her unbuttoned shirt, her nipples at attention in the night air.

"You're gonna take me for a ride on this big old thing, aren't you?"

Nick grinned, hopped on the bike, and kicked the engine to life. Chi-Chi wrapped her arms around Nick's hips, and as they rode through the city streets, her hand found Nick's cock and stroked it slowly and steadily, not stopping even at red lights. Darting dangerously and arrogantly between cars, Nick took a few wrong turns, savoring the rhythm of the road beneath her tires and Chi-Chi's hand. Each sharp swerve made Chi-Chi squeeze a little tighter, stroke a little faster.

"What the hell if I crash," Nick thought. "Damn fine way to go."

Only a public bus could have taken longer to reach Chi-Chi's apartment, an old brick walk-up halfway across town. Between kisses that made her lips bleed, Chi-Chi was just barely able to unlock her door.

"Here, let me help," Nick whispered, "I'm pretty good at getting things to open." She reached down into the leg of her boot, and a quick, sharp click revealed the gleaming edge of a switchblade. She shoved Chi-Chi roughly through her door, tearing open her shirt and cutting her bra off with a swift jerk. Large breasts shook heavily free into Nick's hands, and her fingers eagerly tugged and rolled the dark brown nipples.

Chi-Chi slid against the wall and wrapped one leg around Nick's.

"You like to play rough, don't you?" she asked, running her nails along the back of Nick's neck, where the short hairs grew.

"Only with sluts who jack me off while they ride bitch on my bike," Nick growled, bending to bite Chi-Chi's nipple so hard that she rose up on the tips of her high-heeled shoes. Chi-Chi grabbed a fistful of Nick's hair and pulled her head up to kiss her, sucking Nick's tongue deep into her mouth.

"Riding bitch. Is that what you call it? What else have you got for me to ride?" She groaned in Nick's ear as her hand slid to the bulge in Nick's pants.

"You know damn well what." Nick pushed Chi-Chi's hand away roughly and pulled out her cock. With a heavy and deliberate shove, she forced Chi-Chi to the floor and ground her hips against Chi-Chi's face.

"I'd love to discuss civilization with you now, but I know you're too much of a refined lady to talk with your mouth full."

Chi-Chi dug her nails into the ass of Nick's jeans as she knelt on the kitchen floor. Her lips closed around the head of Nick's cock and she slowly took in the length of it. Nick moaned and braced her hands on the edge of the table. Her hips thrust forward and Chi-Chi gagged from the force of Nick's cock ramming the back of her throat. Her mouth delivering expert head after the hand job on the bike made Nick come in moments, groaning and swearing, the muscles of her ass clenching, her hips bucking.

"Nice appetizer. Now, what does a good girl like you have to offer a hungry butch after a long night out?" Nick grinned down at Chi-Chi's lipstick-smeared face, extending a hand to help her up from her knees. Her cock bobbed eagerly from between the buttons of her jeans.

Standing now, Chi-Chi walked carefully to the fridge. "Well, let me see." She bent over deeply, one hand holding the door for balance. Her ass swayed from side to side as she called out her offerings. "I've got some Caesar salad left over from lunch, and a little bit of cottage cheese."

Nick walked up close behind her, reaching underneath her skirt. She slid her thumb over the smooth crack of Chi-Chi's ass, then flicked her fingers lightly over the damp crotch of her panties.

"I was thinking of something a bit meatier," she hissed between clenched teeth as she pinched the swollen edges of Chi-Chi's inner lips between her thumb and forefinger. "I was hoping you had something you could just warm up for me." Nick wrapped her other arm around the dancer's waist and swung her onto the counter. Chi-Chi's elbows struck the top with a thud and her head hung over the other side, long hair obscuring her face. Her toes barely touched the floor, her hips balanced against the edge, her ass jutted into the air in front of Nick's cock.

"Of course, being a gentleman, I'd be happy to just prepare things myself." Nick spread Chi-Chi's ass cheeks with one large hand and pulled the sodden underwear aside with the other. In one fierce lurch, she entered Chi-Chi up to the base of her cock. The latex balls slapped against the dancer's thighs with each thrust as she heaved herself backward and up, trying to take in even more of Nick.

"That's it, bitch. You wanna ride, do you? Do you? How do you like this? You like to ride bitch, don't you? Don't you, bitch?" With each question, Nick slammed forward hard enough to knock her knees on the counter's edge.

Chi-Chi arched her head, level with the counter, then swung it low again with each driving thrust. Her fists pummeled the wooden cabinet doors. "You know I do. Yes, Nick. Just like that. Just like that. Don't stop, damn you. Don't you dare fucking stop."

Nick wrapped her hands around Chi-Chi's hips, straightened her shoulders, planted her feet firmly on the floor. "No, Babe. Don't you worry, Babe. Daddy's engine never runs out of gas."

from **Fist**

Elaine Miller
for Bet

I fucking *love* a woman who knows what she wants.

She was so wet that my two fingers slid inside her, smooth, like they belonged.

Her eyes were closed, a half-smile was on her lips. The hot, slick, sweet fucking pull of her lit a fire in my belly. I remembered her fingers measuring my wrist earlier, and smiled.

She was tight at first, and I touched her gently, my fingers inside her, flicking up behind her clit, playing with her as she opened to me. One finger, then two, then three...back to one finger sliding in and out so slowly—and she hissed under her breath at me, frustrated, pushing her cunt at my hand, trying to capture more, more.

I rolled her over fast, pivoting her neatly despite the rope at her wrists, and gave her six fast, sharp smacks on her quivering butt. She yelped with the first few and began kicking, so I held her legs for the last two, then rolled her over to face me again. Her round butt was way too tempting, and if I didn't get it out of sight I might spank her all night.

She waited, breathlessly watching, impatiently squirming, as I placed the bottle of lube in a hot water bowl, put a few extra gloves by the bed, and stripped. The tank top came off easily, boots with a bit of effort, then jeans and socks joined the pile on the floor.

I snapped on a glove. When I glanced her way, eyebrow cocked, she flushed a little. Her eyes round and innocent, she bit her lip, pulled her knees up, and slowly parted them. I hurried.

Climbing back on the bed, I touched her hands and arms, checking for temperature difference, ready to shift ropes if need be. As I felt one hand, then the other, she returned the squeeze. Her slim fingers went around my wrist again, an unmistakable gesture of measuring, of gauging the thickness of my wrists and the size of my hands.

She was greedy and opened to me quickly, flowering around me as I fucked her deeper and deeper, doing the holding back for both of us as she thrust toward me. I took my time, making sure she was relaxed, going to three fingers, then four, tucking in my thumb and adding more lube. She was slick and hot and her core was calling to me—then she relaxed suddenly, pulled her knees up a bit more, and went still. She held her breath as I pushed past the last bit of tension and curled inside her, grasped by her wet cunt.

Inside her. Struck by rapture, I could not move at all until she demanded it, couldn't imagine a moment more perfect than this until she proved it to me, pushing herself farther onto me, wrapping her cunt around my forearm as she made a continuous purring sound, groaning with pleasure. I rocked my hand inside her, feeling her respond instantly to my changes of pressure and tempo.

No matter how many times I fist a woman, one thing never changes: the sense of awe I feel as the thickest part of my hand slips past the tension and the last few inches of me disappear inside her of their own accord, slick and with a rush. My hand curls into a fist like a sleeping cat, and her cunt flutters around me, around my wrist. Sometimes she is so tight I can't move for a while, and I sit there, shaken to my core at the trust and raw energy between us. Sometimes she has room inside right away, and I can pump inside her. My mind is entirely wrapped in my fist at times like these: wrapped in my fist and all the way inside her cunt, hot and slick and wet and pulsing. I can fuck forever like this, the familiar burn in my shoulder muscles ignored, almost unnoticed.

I pushed the heel of my left hand against her clit, putting on a bit of pressure—just a little. Her sweet cunt convulsed around my fist again. She sucked in her breath and moved her hips against *that* hand now, grinding her clit against me, spiraling up toward coming.

"Stop."

She blinked at me, hips still moving, faltering only a little. "Don't move. Not even an inch."

I relaxed the pressure on her clit and stopped the motion of my other hand.

"You're doing just fine. You are so fucking hot, such a pretty nasty thing, impaled on my fist." Her breath hissed out, releasing tension with it. "I love it when you want more. Play the game with me."

She relaxed against the bed, opened her legs farther, and concentrated on feeling my hands.

I fucked her hard, suddenly, my fist pushing her limits, stretching her with each thrust. Mouth opened, she stared at the ceiling for a second, making no sound, then gave a muffled shriek with each inward push, louder as I got faster, until she was continuously wailing, stopping only for gasps of air. I caught her at the edge of hyperventilating, eased in and out of her more and more slowly, brought her down, and pulled my hand out of her, just part way.

Gasping, she stared at me with disbelief. I poured a thick stream of warm lube into the convenient channel provided by my curled palm, then around my wrist. I smiled at her, feeling tender, drinking in the sight of her flushed face, lips parted, eyes half-lidded.

"Remember, don't move. Ready?" She started to nod, stopped, and arched her neck as I went in again, unbearably easily this time, feeling no resistance as it seemed she pulled me right to the bottom of her cunt. I replaced my left hand over her clit and pressed as I started fucking her again, slowly at first, then harder and faster, reaching a peak, then more slowly again, then still more slowly as she gasped a wordless protest.

She groaned then as I slid in so slowly it took a full breath cycle to sink all the way into her. She lost control and bucked against my hand.

"I thought you weren't supposed to be moving..." I stopped, let my hand go limp inside her, went with her movements instead of against them so she couldn't catch any friction or pressure, and took my other hand off her clit.

Scream of protest.

I ran my hand along her smooth brown skin until I reached her breast, grasped her erect nipple between two fingers, and rubbed my thumb over it hard. Another gasp and clench, as she pushed her body toward me. I gave her nothing.

I could hear a slight noise and realized she was grinding her teeth.

When a few moments had passed and she had not moved again, I brought my fingers to her clit and began strumming it slowly, trying to tease her into moving. When she was still, only whimpering slightly, I started fucking her again, still moving so easily inside her that I felt I could crawl all the way. She made such beautiful sounds, such cat-in-heat sounds...It was time to up the ante.

"Now I want you to be quiet."

She cast me an incredulous look, more than blunted by her fuzzy expression, but she went silent, only the hiss of her breath, the flaring of her nostrils, and the expression on her face showing what she felt. I pulled her legs up over my shoulders, leaned over her, and fucked her hard again, watching the tug of emotion behind her eyes, which got wider and wider the harder we fucked. After what seemed like an eternity of pushing and pulling, sliding through her in an erotic haze, she whispered something I had to slow my movements to catch.

"Please let me scream," she repeated, and I saw stars.

I felt a snarl involuntarily lift my lip as I let myself go, sliding all the way in with each stroke, watching her yank mindlessly at the rope around her wrists, muscles straining, as she wrapped her strong thighs around me and pulled me closer, shoving back at me, impaling herself on my forearm as I fucked her into a place where she couldn't remember my name or hers. She chanted "Fuck fuck fuck fuck..." each time before she screamed.

I could feel the moment when it was arriving, and I placed my wet thumb on her clit, my left hand pressing into her belly, feeling my fist inside her as it pistoned back and forth. I nudged her clit from side to side in rhythm with my thrusts, and within seconds she sucked in her breath, long and deep, and just fucking exploded, wrapped around my fist so tight I could feel my wrist creak. I felt it deep in my cunt, she came so hard; arched off the bed, stabbing herself on my arm, working her clit against my thumb, shuddering over and over, her cunt pulsing now, beating like a great, slow heart inside her.

Behold the Burning Bush

María Helena Dolan

Sex. Succulent, steamy, absolutely devouring and annihilating sex. That's what María Isabella had been giving me. That's what drove me absolutely insane.

And that's what she is withholding now, in order to make her little prophetic pronouncement come true.

See, when I first spied her dancing to the hot salsero band in the tiny Cubana dyke club on the South Shore, I knew I just had to have her.

I thought, *"Tan caliente."* And then, *"Mujer, estás tan caliente. Y estoy caliente tambien."* This dark, full-figured beauty simply radiated heat, even in the midst of heatedly tropical surroundings. She moved with an internal rhythm that flowed out through her hips, traveled through space, and then sent shock waves through me.

As if we were characters in a bad novel, our eyes met across the dingy little dance floor, and without exchanging words, we knew we'd be sharing fruits from the garden of earthly delights before the night was out.

And so we did. And did again. And again. And again, for three months. But that was her limit. She told me after the first week, *"No puedo ver nadie más que tres meses."* I wasn't to take it personally. She just never could handle being with someone beyond this very set, defined time limit.

Unfortunately, I did take it personally! Everything we did, everything we felt. And, wonder of wonders, after a while, the unbelievably intense sex got to her, too. And it just fried her ass that I'd actually made her feel something.

So, I had to go—despite her telling me over and over as we fucked our brains out:

"¡A! Mamita, tú eres lo mejor, lo mejor! Hay que hacerme. Fuck me and make me come all over your face. *¡Ahora mismo!"*

The best. Yeah, I'm the best. But here I am, riding the rails to work in my little tan uniform, and the woman who's driving me crazy has already got another fool to replace me.

You want to talk bad mood? You want to talk last straw? Man, I could get fired from all the attitude I've been throwing out to the riding public. A guy bumps into me on the platform, and it ain't *"Perdóname."* No, it's *"No me jódas, pendejo!"*

My *bipiaso* starts beeping, and I loudly cuss out my *chipero* neighbor who undoubtedly wants me to do something for him again. And all the time, I'm wearing that unmistakable "City of Miami Transit System Electronic Technician" patch on my shirt.

Carájo! Fuck customer service, fuck these *hijos de putas* who are always whining about losing their fucking fares in the gate, when you know good and goddamn well that they never put the fucking money in the turnstile in the first fuckin' place!

As these and other, less charitable, ruminations course through my preoccupied mind, I feel a light touch against my fingers, which are curled along the smooth chrome surface of the train car's hand rail. Startled, I snatch my hand back and look up into the deepest, darkest pools of ebony ever to grace a woman's face.

You could get lost inside those, I realize with a sharp inhalation. In a milky, melodious voice, with just a hint of an accent, she asks, "Are you troubled, sister? Is there something I can help you with?"

Oh. Yeah. And then I pan out, and take in...her wimple. Her veil. Her entire habit. The best-looking thing I've seen in ages, and she's a fucking bride of Christ! Sighing and cursing my luck, I reply, "I don't think so, Sister."

She sits beside me and clasps my hand between hers, holding it almost as if it were a prayer book. Peering into my palm, she traces the lines across it, sending deliciously shuddering waves of sensation through me. "I can see that you've been disappointed in love. And I can see that you deserve better than you've received. She was not the right woman for you."

Stunned, I want her to continue touching my hand. But what does this nun know about it? Is she a real nun, or is this some elaborately bizarre come-on?

Before I have time to rummage further in my closet of doubts, she takes my hand in hers and delicately and discreetly presses it against her crotch. As though burnt, I yelp and pull away. After all, twelve years of Cuban parochial schooling teaches you to look at women who have taken the veil in a certain way. And this is not that way.

Smiling understandingly, she again takes my hand, again clasps it between her own, and again surreptitiously places it into her lap. This time, I don't pull away.

She looks meaningfully into my eyes and says in that scary, low voice nuns are trained to use on recalcitrant pupils: "Let us go to your place of work. We can be alone there, and I can give you the consolation that you need."

At this, every nerve in my body jumps and twitches and shouts *"¡Ave María y Todos Los Santos!"* and the very hair upon my head is about to stand at attention.

However, being well-trained, I merely swallow hard, nod, and stare at the flooring until the next stop.

I do not have such mundane thoughts as, "This must be a form of sacrilege," or even "I'll get fired if they find us in there together." No, nothing so coherent. Only "OhmyGodOhMyGod *¡¡¡Aiaiaiai!!!"*

In this altered state, we disembark on the platform, and I half escort her, half drag myself down into the bowels of the station, my keys jangling at my waist, echoing the jingling made by the rosary beads looped around her waist. We enter into a labyrinth of doors bearing forbidding messages such as Off limits to Unauthorized Personnel, *¡Peligro! No Pasa* and Danger! 750 Volts.

I use the fat key embedded with coded spots to open a security door, and we enter what transit workers affectionately call "The Underworld." Few people know that this area exists, and even fewer know what these portals open onto.

It is indeed another realm, of concrete, conduit, copper connectors, blinking LEDs, clicking relays, and humming equipment. I usually enjoy hearing this cacophonous din upon arriving; I feel like a returning sovereign being greeted by hordes of adulating subjects.

This morning, though, it's all changed. Uncertain and becoming increasingly nervous, I turn to explain what some of the equipment does. But before I can say anything, she draws me to her with surprisingly strong arms and sticks her tongue into my open-and-about-to-speak mouth.

I'm startled and a little taken aback. But in the next moment, I am overpowered by her skill and forcefulness and simply give myself over to her.

Now there are long, long moments of mouths and hands and tongues and breasts all intertwined and pressing with great ardor. The room temperature shoots up by about twenty degrees, as do our body temperatures. *Fiebre.* I could perish happily in this now-sweltering embrace.

The kissing seems to go on forever. Lips pressed against each other, lips apart, tongues entwined, we are like tiny snakes seeking warmth.

Each moment is a revelation, a new mystery, a soul-shaking and heart-pounding act.

Finally, after hours or minutes or decades, we move in silent concert to the work table against the wall. We are in complete accord as she lowers herself onto the formica-topped, unyielding surface. Frantically, I divest myself of the habitually hanging multiple key rings, beeper, two-way radio, flashlight, cell phone, and other work implements clipped to my crowded belt.

Now unimpeded, my hand—of its own volition—somehow finds itself pulling up the flowing skirt of her habit. Beneath, she wears nothing but a simple garter belt to hold up her sensible black stockings.

But this presents a more exciting vista than the most whorish lingerie imaginable. And I can smell her excitement as it begins to seep from the center of her. Suddenly ravenous, I must taste her.

"Show me, sister," I murmur in devout prayer. *"Muéstreme."* Her hands answer by traveling to that sacred mound and then creating a little cathedral of fingertips imitating flying buttresses, pulling the outer lips aside to reveal the sacred vestibule. My gaze travels longingly down the contours of her hallowed landscape, until finally I find what she displays.

A small moan escapes from my clenched lips as I behold the very seat of her power. The sacristy lamp is lit, blood-red, the sacred sacrament is present. This is indeed the fire hole, the birthplace of the gods, the center of the universe. This is the mystery of the Goddess incarnate, which her priestess now proffers so readily.

A dumbstruck acolyte, I wordlessly reach my hand to lightly stroke the exquisitely soft fur surmounting the sacred grotto. Before I even realize it, my head joins my hand, and I reverently kiss the furred altar cloth. Already trembling, she releases her scapular hold and moves her hands, ready to give herself up to the ineffable pleasure. And pleasure her I shall, with every ounce of my fervent being.

My mouth kisses lower, my lips brushing the very root where her clit grows. She cries out and opens her legs wider. *"¡Aí, aí Madre de Dios, aí Jesus, aííí!"* Her ejaculations begin to spout in a gushing torrent.

I kiss down those glistening lips, the smell and feel of her igniting fires all over my now-searing flesh.

One hand reaches under her gown for an unfettered nipple, the stab of sensation piercing her and causing her to cry aloud again. The other rests on her root chakra, my forefinger and thumb peeling the small hood back and apart for greater depth of sensation.

My tongue has been kicking like a mare in heat, pent up in her stall.

Finally, I can loose her in those running fields! The good sister's clit engorges even more as I gallop free across that wondrous plain, full of folds and hills and crevices.

She continuously moans now as I run down her ravine and then into that sacred well, drinking in the knowledge of life itself.

In and out I run, time and again, my fingers working the base of her clit and my other hand kneading her breast. With each thrust of my charging tongue, I taste her river as it begins to gush, the sweetest, lightest, creamiest beurre blanc any chef has ever seen.

"*¡Aí, chíngame. ¡Chíngame!* Fuck me!" she demands frantically. I lift my charging tongue to her raging clit and begin those long strides back and forth. My hand leaves off the fulsome breast and slowly, I begin to ease two fingers into her aching, arching cunt. She screams and thrashes her hips harder, feeling the force of it.

I shudder with the power of entering that most sacred of objects, the woman's body. I become transfixed, only lightly stirring this fantastic cauldron. About to burn up with the heat, she commands, "*Cómame. Chíngame.* Fuck me. Fuck me hard!"

And of course, so commanded, I must comply. I reach into her with great force and then pull almost all the way out. And reach and pull. And reach and pull, with the heat and force of a devouring forest fire, hot winds driving at my back. I am frantically trying to outswim the fury of an approaching hurricane set to devastate this exposed coastline.

As the pleasure intensifies at her wilding clit, she suddenly seeks to get away, to avoid the tidal wave about to crash upon the beach stretching below.

This I cannot allow. Mercilessly, relentlessly, I run her down like a pack of Diana's hounds who've caught the blood spore. Her roaring just spurs me on. I chase and chase, with ever-shortening strides.

There, at the cliff's very edge, I catch her, and we dive into that deepest of ocean canyons. She writhes and moans and sprays my face with that most vivifying of juices, thrashing like a barracuda who has been hauled to shore following a fierce struggle. Gasping and groaning, she holds my wrist so that I no longer thrust down her pulsing tunnel.

From a great distance, I hear her begin to whisper endearments, entreaties, enspherements. But my tongue is not ready to relinquish her freedom, and I keep licking until the saddle is hard again and ready for more mounting.

"*Estás matándome!*" she admonishes. But the way she lays her head back down and spreads her legs a little farther betrays her collusion in this terrible crime. Duty bound, I will not cease my efforts until she finally pushes me away. Because this is what we were both born for. This is the Great Mystery. This is life itself.

My engrossed reverie is shattered when the two-way radio begins squawking my call sign: "801. 801! Report in, 801." Shaking with the incredible effort first to come to the surface, and then to form a coherent sentence, I lift my head and hand up and grab the braying black box.

It's an annoying parasite that is usually welded to my resentful hip. It forces responsiveness from me, seemingly, whenever I begin to eat lunch, look at the women walking through the station, or sit down on the toilet seat.

So naturally, the semi-indecipherable but definitely not ignorable voice of Central Control must intrude NOW. ¡Jesus!

"This is 801. I'm 10-8 at Coconut Grove."

"Give us a call at -3406."

"Affirmative."

Damn. Damndamndamn. The spell is surely broken.

Oh no! She's pulled her dress down and is getting off the table. Before I can preempt this horror, she lays a finger to my lips and says, "I'll see you on the train again sometime, querida."

What? Wait! We're not finished! I...

"Sometime," she calls calmly over her shoulder as she exits the room, setting off the intrusion alarm. Shit! I have to reset this piece of crap and explain to Central why I set it off, as well as pick up my work orders for the day. Not to mention figuring out how I can possibly survive the next eight hours down here, her smell and taste still with me and my own fires unabated.

¡Aii! Life can be so oddly unpredictable in the tropics.

Honest

Cynthia Greenberg

I can't tell stories. we really did those reckless things and we really did try. not to. to undo them. to smooth over the ruptures they caused. we really berated ourselves and shamed each other for the carelessness we shared. we really couldn't stop. we really rented any number of hotel rooms and booked random flights. we really picked up in the middle of our days and lusted into the night. we really drove down winding highways in a drunken haze. we really fucked more than we rode. we really misbehaved in restaurants and theaters and shops. we really disregarded our entire lives. we really called in late or sick or didn't show up at all. we really lost our jobs. we really stopped eating at regular times. we really soiled endless sets of sheets. we really forgot our pets, our politics, our friends. we really jonesed and lied. we really fettered ourselves to our fetishes. we really dressed up to lie down. we really sulked and pouted and whined. we really fled. we really hid. we really walked the streets of your city or mine. we really saw nothing but smut. we really spent all our dollars and borrowed on them. we really leaned, faltered, fell.

I can't tell stories but you were a boy and I was a girl. or you were a man and I wasn't. or you were where and how your cock was hung and I was always low and ready and not dry. you said things, I heard things, we crashed into each other. your body was the same and your mind is different, but we crossed the same lines. you have a fist and I hold your hand. you push and I resist. it doesn't matter what names you call things because you call and I answer. I see you underneath your skin. you take flesh and make it fiction, and I invent what we lack. it doesn't matter what was said or what people overheard. we were there and it will stay. our madness, our pleasures, our trusts. the fissures we played.

I can't tell stories but I read myself each night: violence is not just something two bodies commit in the dark. it is a yearning and the danger of desire sitting up between us demanding a fare.

About the Editors

JENIFER LEVIN is the author of four novels, *Water Dancer, Snow, Shimoni's Lover* and *The Sea of Light,* and a short story collection, *Love and Death and Other Disasters.* She lives in New York.

TRISTAN TAORMINO is series editor of the annual collection *Best Lesbian Erotica,* for which she has collaborated with guest editors Heather Lewis, Jewelle Gomez, and Jenifer Levin. She is the author of *The Ultimate Guide to Anal Sex for Women* (Cleis Press). She is co-editor of *A Girl's Guide to Taking over the World: Writings from the Girl Zine Revolution* (St. Martin's Press, 1997) and *Ritual Sex* (Rhinoceros Books, 1996) a collection of writing on sex, religion, and spirituality. She is also publisher and editrix of the pansexual erotic magazine *Pucker Up.* Her writing appears in several publications and anthologies, including *The Femme Mystique, Heatwave: Women in Love and Lust, Sex Spoken Here, Chick-Lit 2,* and *Virgin Territory II,* as well as *On Our Backs, Sojourner, The Boston Phoenix, The Advocate, X-X-X Fruit, Venus Infers,* and *Blue Blood. The Advocate* named her one of the Best and Brightest Gay and Lesbian People Under 30. She lives in Brooklyn.

About the Authors

TONI AMATO is a working-class butch dyke, living in rural Vermont with her wife and two dogs. Her writing has appeared in *Leatherwomen II*. "Ridin' Bitch" is an excerpt from her erotic novel, *Mama's Boy*.

GWENDOLYN BIKIS is a white dyke living in Oakland, California, where she teaches literacy in adult schools. Excerpts from her novel *Soldiers* have appeared in *The Persistent Desire, Catalyst, Conditions, Sleeping with Dionysus, Sister/Stranger, Close Calls,* and *Does Your Mama Know?* She is the recipient of the John Hay Preston Erotic Writing Award.

In addition to making girls come, CARELLIN BROOKS is a writer and columnist with a fatal weakness for old-school butches. She is currently working on an anthology of stories about bad jobs for Arsenal Pulp Press.

TEE CHANDLER is a founding member of Sexrites, Britain's first lesbian sex writing group. She co-authored *Lesbians Talk...Violent Relationships*. She co-wrote and jointly directed *Shades of Desire*, a Channel 4 film celebrating interracial lesbian desire. Her work has appeared in *Diva, Common Denominator,* and many poetry anthologies. "Juice" is for Lesley.

CHRYSTOS has been a proud lesbian for thirty-two years. She is a treaty and prisoners' rights activist who performs her work internationally. She is the author of *Not Vanishing, Dream On, In Her I Am, Fugitive Colors,* and *Fire Power.* She is widely anthologized and has received many awards and grants, including The Audre Lorde International Poetry Competition and The Sappho Award of Distinction from the Astraea National Lesbian Action Foundation.

PAULA KAYE CLEARWATER lives in the foothills of the White Mountains, where she shares a country home with her partner, a dog, and some chickens. The winters are long and cold. She keeps warm by splitting wood, sitting by the fire, and writing erotica. Another of her short stories appears in *Heatwave: Women in Love and Lust.*

JANE DELYNN is the author of the novels *Don Juan in the Village, Real Estate, In Thrall,* and *Some Do.* Her collection of stories and essays, *Bad Sex Is Good,* will be published in 1998 by Painted Leaf Press. She has published in *The New York Times, The Washington Post, Mademoiselle, Glamour, The Paris Review, The New York Observer, Redbook, Avenue, Christopher Street,* and *The Advocate.*

MARÍA HELENA DOLAN knows that all roads—as well as intergalactic coordinates—lead to Atlanta. Labeled the "Mouth of the South" by *Out Magazine,* she lives among cultivated tropical fecundity with felines who harbor schemes for total global domination. She's still making the trains run on time as well as writing a novel.

JAMIE GABRIEL lives in Boston. By afternoon and by night she is a science nerd, slavishly doing research for the betterment of humankind. But in the wee hours of the morning a different kind of creativity is unleashed. This is her first published story.

RUTH GIFFORD lives in suburban Southern California with her wife atara, her two step-children, and three mandatory cats. "Just Drops" is her first published story.

CYNTHIA GREENBERG is a displaced California poet and troublemaker living in New York City. Her work has appeared in *Nice Jewish Girls: Growing Up in America.* She has an abiding interest in language, literacy, and activism. She is currently at work on an anthology about lesbians and loss.

KATHE IZZO is a poet and performance artist currently living in Provincetown, passionately riding both sides of the tracks in every way since the day she was born. Mother of three daughters, she is the founder of the Shadow Writing Project, a writing school for youth-at-risk, and is editor of *Flicker,* a journal of teen writing. Her work has been published in *xxxfruit* and *Meet Me at the Bottom of the Pool,* published by Serpents Tail Press. She is founding director of Thalassa Writing Retreats, a solitary teaching retreat for poets.

DORIAN KEY is a nice boy from San Francisco. Her work appears in *Strategic Sex* and *50/50 Magazine.* She is co-editor of *boy: the zine for boy-dykes, tranny-boys, butches, transfags and those who love them.*

KARLYN LOTNEY produces and emcees her campy erotic cabaret *In Bed with Fairy Butch,* leads instructional sex workshops, and publishes her advice column, "Ask Fairy Butch," in *Curve, Oblivion,* and *Paramour* magazines. Contact her at FairyButch@aol.com to receive her free sex tip/event e-mailer; she's taking her show on the road!

RENITA L. MARTIN is a Boston-based writer and performance artist whose work has appeared in *Aché Journal, Women's Words, The Boston Globe, Paramour,* and *Does Your Mama Know?* She has traveled nationally with "Rhythms Visions Never Do Be Finished," a choreopoem based on her book of poetry of the same title. She is founder and director of Voices from the River: Boston Women's Gospel Choir and Rhythms Visions Production Company, a nonprofit organization devoted to producing significant works by artists of color.

ELAINE MILLER, having been told since childhood that she is a queer sort, now makes it a way of life. Besides being the full-time editor of *Diversity Magazine,* she admits responsibility for quite a number of stories, articles, and spoken-word nasties. This marks her first book publication.

BONNIE J. MORRIS is a women's studies professor and the author of two books on Jewish women's history. Her lesbian essays appear in over twenty-five anthologies. Her zest-filled adventures include traveling around the world by ship, touring with one-woman plays, appearing in the film *Contact* with Jodie Foster, and working at nearly every women's music festival in the country.

PEGGY MUNSON was born in Normal, Illinois. Her work has appeared in various journals. She has held residency fellowships at Cottages at Hedgebrook and the Ragdale Foundation, where this story came to fruition. Currently at work on a collection of stories, she lives in Rhode Island with her big gray dog.

JANE PERKINS is a writer living in Brooklyn, New York. She has been published in various anthologies and is working on her first novel.

DEBORAH L. REPPLIER is a poet who likes to blur the boundaries with prose, exploring the continuum of past/present, memory/fantasy, and that sometimes space of reality. Her work has been previously published by *Sojourner,* The Women's Press of Toronto, the National Library of Poetry, and *Common Lives Lesbian Lives.*

HEATHER L. SEGGEL is a juggler, armchair sexologist, and frequent flier in the zine world. She lives in the Northern California redwoods, working as a bookseller and sex toy reviewer, and trying to improve her baking skills.

KIM YAGED is an award-winning playwright whose work has been performed in New York, Michigan, and Illinois, including various venues throughout Chicago. In addition to appearing in numerous newspapers and journals, her writings have been internationally anthologized. She is currently an M.F.A. student in playwriting at the University of Michigan.

Great Erotic Reading!

Best Lesbian Erotica and *Best Gay Erotica* feature the steamiest, most thought-provoking lesbian and gay sex writing you'll find. Each year, guest judges selected from the queer literary world review the year's best erotica and choose the final collection, representing a wide range of styles and voices. Once again, we present the best in sexy, literate queer writing—sometimes dark, sometimes perverse, often strange and irreverent, frequently unconventional, but always compelling, provocative, and hot.

BEST LESBIAN EROTICA 1998
Tristan Taormino, Series Editor
Selected and introduced by Jenifer Levin
$14.95 ISBN: 1-57344-032-9

BEST LESBIAN EROTICA 1997
Edited by Tristan Taormino
Selected by Jewelle Gomez
$14.95 ISBN: 1-57344-065-5

BEST LESBIAN EROTICA 1996
Edited by Tristan Taormino
Selected by Heather Lewis
$12.95 ISBN: 1-57344-054-X

BEST GAY EROTICA 1998
Richard Labonté, Series Editor
Selected and introduced
by Christopher Bram
$14.95 ISBN: 1-57344-031-0

BEST GAY EROTICA 1997
Edited by Richard Labonté
Selected and introduced
by Douglas Sadownick
$14.95 ISBN: 1-57344-067-1

BEST GAY EROTICA 1996
Edited by Michael Ford
Selected and introduced by Scott Heim
$12.95 ISBN: 1-57344-052-3

AVAILABLE AT YOUR FAVORITE BOOKSTORE & FROM CLEIS PRESS

How to Order
- **Phone:**   1-800-780-2279 or (415) 575-4700
  Monday - Friday, 9 AM - 5 PM Pacific Standard Time
- **Fax:**   (415) 575-4705
- **Mail:**   Cleis Press
  P.O. Box 14684, San Francisco, California 94114
- **E-mail:**   Cleis@aol.com

Turn the page for more great sex books from Cleis Press...

Great Sex Manuals!

The Ultimate Guide to Anal Sex for Women

Tristan Taormino
$14.95 ISBN: 1-57344-028-0

   The Ultimate Guide to Anal Sex for Women is the first self-help book on anal sex for women. Accurate how-to advice is combined with interesting, eye-catching sidebars—myths, excerpts of erotic stories, and colorful narratives illustrating sexual techniques. User-friendly, sexy, honest, and fun, *The Ultimate Guide to Anal Sex for Women* offers comprehensive information on all aspects of anal eroticism and anal health—for all women, heterosexual, lesbian, and bisexual. This attractive, upbeat guide covers anatomy, taboos and myths, fantasy, genderbending, and power play; latex, lube, and toys; relaxation exercises; analingus, penetration, including fisting; and anal health. Bibliography, resources, index.

The New Good Vibrations Guide to Sex

Tips and Techniques from America's Favorite Sex-Toy Store
Second Edition
Cathy Winks and Anne Semans

                           "The Best Sex Manual Ever Written"— *The Advocate*
   Recommended by medical professionals and sex therapists. Ten years of selling sex toys in a women-owned vibrator store, Good Vibrations, have given authors Anne Semans and Cathy Winks a unique perspective on sex. After talking to thousands of men and women about sex, they've learned what real people enjoy doing in bed and what information can help anyone achieve a happier, more satisfying sex life. This invaluable bedside companion is the single best reference guide to expressing and sharing sexual pleasure ever published.

Books from Cleis

Sex Guides

Good Sex: Real Stories from Real People, second edition
by Julia Hutton.
ISBN: 1-57344-000-0
14.95 paper.

The New Good Vibrations Guide to Sex: Tips and techniques from America's favorite sex-toy store, second edition
by Cathy Winks and Anne Semans.
ISBN: 1-57344-069-8
21.95 paper.

The Ultimate Guide to Anal Sex for Women
by Tristan Taormino.
ISBN: 1-57344-028-0
14.95 paper.

Sexual Politics

Annie Sprinkle: Post-Porn Modernist—My Twenty-Five Years as a Multimedia Whore
by Annie Sprinkle.
ISBN: 1-57344-039-6
19.95 paper

Forbidden Passages: Writings Banned in Canada
introductions by Pat Califia and Janine Fuller.
Lambda Literary Award Winner.
ISBN: 1-57344-019-1
14.95 paper.

Public Sex: The Culture of Radical Sex
by Pat Califia.
ISBN: 0-939416-89-1
12.95 paper.

Real Live Nude Girl: Chronicles of Sex-Positive Culture
by Carol Queen.
ISBN: 1-57344-073-6.
14.95 paper.

Sex Work: Writings by Women in the Sex Industry
edited by Frédérique Delacoste and Priscilla Alexander.
ISBN: 0-939416-11-5
16.95 paper.

Susie Bright's Sexual Reality: A Virtual Sex World Reader
by Susie Bright.
ISBN: 0-939416-59-X
9.95 paper.

Susie Bright's Sexwise
by Susie Bright.
ISBN: 1-57344-002-7
10.95 paper.

Susie Sexpert's Lesbian Sex World
by Susie Bright.
ISBN: 0-939416-35-2
9.95 paper.

Erotic Literature

Best Gay Erotica 1998
selected by Christopher Bram, edited by Richard Labonté.
ISBN: 1-57344-031-0
14.95 paper.

Best Gay Erotica 1997
selected by Douglas Sadownick, edited by Richard Labonté.
ISBN: 1-57344-067-1
14.95 paper.

Best Gay Erotica 1996,
selected by Scott Heim, edited by Michael Ford.
ISBN: 1-57344-052-3
12.95 paper.

Best Lesbian Erotica 1998
selected by Jenifer Levin, edited by Tristan Taormino.
ISBN: 1-57344-032-9
14.95 paper.

Best Lesbian Erotica 1997
selected by Jewelle Gomez, edited by Tristan Taormino.
ISBN: 1-57344-065-5
14.95 paper.

The Leather Daddy and the Femme: An Erotic Novel
by Carol Queen.
ISBN: 1-57344-037-X
14.00 paper.

Serious Pleasure: Lesbian Erotic Stories and Poetry edited by the Sheba Collective.
ISBN: 0-939416-45-X
9.95 paper.

Gender Transgression

Body Alchemy: Transsexual Portraits by Loren Cameron. Lambda Literary Award Winner.
ISBN: 1-57344-062-0
24.95 paper.

Dagger: On Butch Women edited by Roxxie, Lily Burana, Linnea Due.
ISBN: 0-939416-82-4
14.95 paper.

I Am My Own Woman: The Outlaw Life of Charlotte von Mahlsdorf translated by Jean Hollander.
ISBN: 1-57344-010-8
12.95 paper.

PoMoSexuals: Challenging Assumptions about Gender and Sexuality edited by Carol Queen and Lawrence Schimel. Preface by Kate Bornstein.
ISBN: 1-57344-074-4
14.95 paper.

Sex Changes: The Politics of Transgenderism by Pat Califia.
ISBN: 1-57344-072-8
16.95 paper.

Switch Hitters: Lesbians Write Gay Male Erotica and Gay Men Write Lesbian Erotica edited by Carol Queen and Lawrence Schimel.
ISBN: 1-57344-021-3
12.95 paper.

Lesbian and Gay Studies

An American Dyke Dream: Home edited by Susan Fox Rogers.
ISBN: 1-57344-036-1
14.95 paper

The Case of the Good-For-Nothing Girlfriend by Mabel Maney. Lambda Literary Award Nominee.
ISBN: 0-939416-91-3
10.95 paper.

The Case of the Not-So-Nice Nurse by Mabel Maney. Lambda Literary Award Nominee.
ISBN: 0-939416-76-X
9.95 paper.

Nancy Clue and the Hardly Boys in A Ghost in the Closet by Mabel Maney. Lambda Literary Award Nominee.
ISBN: 1-57344-012-4
10.95 paper.

Different Daughters: A Book by Mothers of Lesbians, second edition edited by Louise Rafkin.
ISBN: 1-57344-050-7
12.95 paper.

Different Mothers: Sons & Daughters of Lesbians Talk about Their Lives edited by Louise Rafkin. Lambda Literary Award Winner.
ISBN: 0-939416-41-7
9.95 paper.

A Lesbian Love Advisor by Celeste West.
ISBN: 0-939416-26-3
9.95 paper.

On the Rails: A Memoir second edition, by Linda Niemann. Introduction by Leslie

Marmon Silko.
ISBN: 1-57344-064-7.
14.95 paper.

Queer Dog: Homo Pup Poetry edited by Gerry Gomez Pearlberg.
ISBN: 1-57344-071-X.
12.95. paper.

Vampires & Horror

Brothers of the Night: Gay Vampire Stories edited by Michael Rowe and Thomas S. Roche.
ISBN: 1-57344-025-6
14.95 paper.

Dark Angels: Lesbian Vampire Stories edited by Pam Keesey. Lambda Literary Award Nominee.
ISBN 1-7344-014-0
10.95 paper.

Daughters of Darkness: Lesbian Vampire Stories edited by Pam Keesey.
ISBN: 0-939416-78-6
12.95 paper.

Vamps: An Illustrtated History of the Femme Fatale by Pam Keesey.
ISBN: 1-57344-026-4
21.95.

Sons of Darkness: Tales of Men, Blood and Immortality edited by Michael Rowe and Thomas S. Roche. Lambda Literary Award Nominee.
ISBN: 1-57344-059-0
12.95 paper.

Women Who Run with the Werewolves: Tales of Blood, Lust and Metamorphosis
edited by Pam Keesey.
Lambda Literary Award Nominee.
ISBN: 1-57344-057-4
12.95 paper.

Debut Literature
Marianne Faithfull's Cigarette: Poems
Gerry Gomez Pearlberg.
ISBN: 1-57344-034-5
12.95 paper

Memory Mambo
by Achy Obejas. Lambda Literary Award Winner.
ISBN: 1-57344-017-5
12.95 paper.

We Came All the Way from Cuba So You Could Dress Like This?: Stories
by Achy Obejas.
Lambda Literary Award Nominee.
ISBN: 0-939416-93-X
10.95 paper.

Seeing Dell
by Carol Guess.
ISBN: 1-57344-023-X
12.95 paper.

World Literature
A Forbidden Passion
by Cristina Peri Rossi.
ISBN: 0-939416-68-9
9.95 paper.

Half a Revolution: Contemporary Fiction by Russian Women
edited by Masha Gessen.
ISBN 1-57344-006-X
$12.95 paper.

The Little School: Tales of Disappearance and Survival in Argentina
by Alicia Partnoy.
ISBN: 0-939416-07-7
9.95 paper.

Peggy Deery: An Irish Family at War
by Nell McCafferty.
ISBN: 0-939416-39-5
9.95 paper.

Thrillers & Dystopias
Another Love
by Erzsébet Galgóczi.
ISBN: 0-939416-51-4
8.95 paper.

Dirty Weekend: A Novel of Revenge
by Helen Zahavi.
ISBN: 0-939416-85-9
10.95 paper.

Only Lawyers Dancing
by Jan McKemmish.
ISBN: 0-939416-69-7
9.95 paper.

The Wall
by Marlen Haushofer.
ISBN: 0-939416-54-9
9.95 paper.

Politics of Health
The Absence of the Dead Is Their Way of Appearing
by Mary Winfrey Trautmann.
ISBN: 0-939416-04-2
8.95 paper.

Don't: A Woman's Word
by Elly Danica.
ISBN: 0-939416-22-0
8.95 paper

Voices in the Night: Women Speaking About Incest
edited by Toni A.H. McNaron and Yarrow Morgan.
ISBN: 0-939416-02-6
9.95 paper.

With the Power of Each Breath: A Disabled Women's Anthology
edited by Susan Browne, Debra Connors, and Nanci Stern.
ISBN: 0-939416-06-9
10.95 paper.

Comix
Dyke Strippers: Lesbian Cartoonists A to Z
edited by Roz Warren.
ISBN: 1-57344-008-6
16.95 paper.

The Night Audrey's Vibrator Spoke: A Stonewall Riots Collection
by Andrea Natalie.
Lambda Literary Award Nominee.
ISBN: 0-939416-64-6
8.95 paper.

Revenge of Hothead Paisan: Homicidal Lesbian Terrorist
by Diane DiMassa.
Lambda Literary Award Nominee.
ISBN: 1-57344-016-7
16.95 paper.

Travel & Cooking
Betty and Pansy's Severe Queer Review of New York
by Betty Pearl and Pansy.
ISBN: 1-57344-070-1
10.95 paper.

Betty and Pansy's Severe Queer Review of San Francisco
by Betty Pearl and Pansy.
ISBN: 1-57344-056-6
10.95 paper.

Food for Life & Other Dish
edited by Lawrence Schimel.
ISBN: 1-57344-061-2
14.95 paper.